Healthy Caregiving

PERSPECTIVES FOR CARING PROFESSIONALS IN COMPANY WITH

HENRI J. M. NOUWEN

Michelle O'Rourke

Foreword by Wayne Muller

TWENTY-THIRD PUBLICATIONS

NOVALIS

© 2020 Novalis Publishing Inc.

Cover image: Matt Chapman (mattchapman.myportfolio.com)
Layout: Audrey Wells

Published by Novalis

Publishing Office
1 Eglinton Avenue East, Suite 800
Toronto, Ontario, Canada
M4P 3A1
www.novalis.ca

Head Office
4475 Frontenac Street
Montréal, Québec, Canada
H2H 2S2

Library and Archives Canada Cataloguing in Publication

Title: Healthy caregiving : perspectives for caring professionals in company with
Henri J.M. Nouwen / Michelle O'Rourke ; foreword by Wayne Muller.
Names: O'Rourke, Michelle, author. | Muller, Wayne, 1953- writer of foreword.
Identifiers: Canadiana 20200152084 | ISBN 9782896887835 (softcover)
Subjects: LCSH: Human services personnel—Health and hygiene. | LCSH:
Medical personnel—Health and hygiene.
Classification: LCC HV40.35 .O76 2020 | DDC 361.3—dc23

Published in the United States by
TWENTY-THIRD PUBLICATIONS
One Montauk Avenue, Suite 200
New London, CT 06320
(860) 437-3012 or (800) 321-0411
www.twentythirdpublications.com
ISBN: 978-1-62785-528-0

Printed in Canada.

We acknowledge the support of the Government of Canada.

5 4 3 2 1   24   23   22   21   20

Contents

Dedication

To my father,
George "Geo" Zimmer
(1936–2016),
who taught me so much about
living well, caring well and dying well

Acknowledgements

After undertaking some thesis research in 2007, diving deeply into the life and writings of Henri Nouwen, I found my own personal and professional life to be transformed. Although I never met Henri in person, I somehow feel as though I know him, and I believe that his spirit guides my work and, in particular, this project.

This project would not have happened without the support and foresight of the Henri Nouwen Society. In its effort to introduce Henri to new audiences and further the legacy and reach of his life and writings, the Society has chosen one area of its focus to be the important work of supporting caregivers. An initial set of resources was developed in partnership with Church Health in Memphis, geared towards supporting those who care for family members and loved ones. Upon the success of the *Courage for Caregivers* series, a need was identified to do the same for those who choose caring as a profession. I was honoured to be chosen to take part in this important project. Special thanks to Karen Pascal, Executive Director of the Henri Nouwen Society, who believed wholeheartedly in the project and in me. Thanks also to Colette, Wil and Liz from the Society office, as well as Sally Keefe Cohen, Marjorie Thompson, Sue Mosteller and all of the members of the board of directors. In particular, we all thank Stronger Philanthropy for the generous funding grant which has allowed this project to flourish.

Much gratitude is extended to my husband, Tom, for his ongoing encouragement and love, and for permission to allow me to share his own story of caregiver fatigue. I am also grateful for the love and support of our children, Matt, Sarah, Rebecca and Katie, and their partners, and my extended family and friends. A special thanks to those who offered suggestions and feedback along the way, and to those who shared their stories with me and allowed them to be published, including Susan, Bridget, MaryBeth, Vivianne, Elyse, Kim and Michael. Also, deep gratitude is extended to all of the caregivers I have met or worked with, who have helped me to understand their issues, needs and stories. Most of all, I carry a deep appreciation for all of the people I have had the privilege to care for, who have taught me so much and helped me to become the person I am today. In particular, I recognize those whose stories are contained in this book.

A special thank you goes out to Joseph Sinasac and his team from Bayard/Novalis, my publisher and distributor for many years, who continue to support my writing and speaking endeavours. I am also extremely grateful to Wayne Muller for writing such a beautiful foreword. Wayne's books have been instrumental in my own growth, personally and professionally, and I am thrilled to have his wisdom be such a special part of this book. Wayne enjoyed a wonderful friendship with Henri, and that connection makes his contribution even more exceptional.

Thank you to authors Shane Sinclair, Matt Licata, Jeff Foster, Lorraine Wright, Amy Wrzeniewski and the many publishers who have granted me permission to quote the work of so many excellent writers and experts in this field. May we all continue to follow our particular paths in helping others to live and work with compassion, and to care for themselves deeply as they care for others.

Foreword

Healthy Caregiving is a priceless, timely collection of thoughtful, unhurried wonderings we desperately need to help us clarify the essential nature of Care. Michelle O'Rourke – through her diverse roles as an innovator in hospice programming, dedicating time in deep collaboration with people in palliative care and oncology, and as a nurse, author, wife and mother of four – invites us to explore, with remarkably careful attention, how we can both generously and sustainably serve the very real needs of others, without unnecessarily sacrificing our own well-being in the process. She accurately describes, through cautionary tales which may be uncomfortably familiar to many of us, how common it is for many good-hearted, well-intended people to become so weary, depleted, even destroyed as we frantically react to ever-expanding demands of a world eternally in need of more and more of our Care.

I am exceedingly grateful that Michelle insists we attempt to discern what we mean when we use the terms *Care* and *Caregiver*. What is Care? How does it work? From where does it arise? How does it move in and through us? How is Care "used"? And does Care increase, replenish or diminish us if we constantly offer it to others? *Especially* if we have not yet found peace with the practice of offering that same Care to ourselves. As those chosen to serve, how do we locate a place of peace that passes understanding, to Care with and for one another in ways in which we all feel some benefit, grace and healing?

9

After writing the book *Sabbath*, and following it with *A Life of Being, Having and Doing Enough*, I received countless invitations to visit nurses, doctors, teachers, clergy, parents, social workers, therapists, non-profit administrators – all of whom feel robbed of the Time they need to do the work they feel called to do. One cannot be a healer, or hear the story beneath the story, or listen to unspoken truths aching to be named, without the gently fertile soil of unhurried Time. Everything precious – love, care, friendship, healing, trust, honesty, community, integrity, creativity, imagination, beauty – can only flourish when planted in the easy, undirected, unrushed garden of wandering in Time.

As that Time is slowly being drained from our ever-busier lives, everything we hold sacred, all things precious, beautiful and meaningful are disappearing from our lives – a little more every day. We do not speak of this; it is too much to bear. We blame ourselves; if only we can learn to be more productive. Perhaps then we can reclaim all the Time we have lost. Yet, this is not about our success or failure. It is a shift in value. Where there were once shelves of self-help books, there are now manuals on "How To Get More Done." If we can work faster than machines, maybe they will let us stay!

But as human beings – even as beloved children of a loving Creator, children with whom that Creator is so very well pleased – we cannot do more than we can do. We invariably come up against a moment when we have nothing left to give. And if we land in that horrific moment when we are still expected to Care for dozens more people, for 20 more hours, yet have nothing to offer – what can we possibly do?

One choice – sadly, the most common – is to offer the best we have. We give them our dishonest kindness. We give what we do not have to give. We offer a counterfeit compassion, something we hope and pray looks enough like Care to pass. We try so very hard to appear as if we are offering them genuine, heartfelt Care. After all, that is our heart's most authentic desire. Why can we not simply will this to be true?

Michelle O'Rourke is inspiring in her clear articulation of this deeper scarcity, this growing pressure for *sacrifice as demonstrable evidence of our value*:

> The systems we work in can certainly be a cause of stress. These include the many bureaucracies and organizations that support health care, social services, education, churches and other institutions providing care for others. Front-line caregiving becomes more burdensome with the added stresses of deadlines, paperwork, time constraints, quality indicators, metrics and other work pressures dictated by the structures and policies in place. The environment of doing more with less, and seeing the lives of those we serve affected by lean budgets and cutbacks, can take its toll on us. I believe that another way that we build resilience is to try to let go of the things we have little or no control over, and choose to concentrate on what we *can* control, which for the most part is the way we respond directly to the people in our care. Being mindful, positive and present can go a long way in helping to keep things in perspective. Henri shares some wisdom that may help:

> > *One of life's great questions centers not on what happens to us, but rather, how we will live in and through whatever happens. We cannot change most circumstances in our lives … Very little of what I have lived, in fact, has to do with what I have decided – whom I have known, where I came into the world, what personality tendencies have taken hold.*

> > *Our choice, then, often revolves around not what has happened or will happen to us, but how we will relate to life's turns and circumstances. Put another way: Will I relate to my life resentfully or gratefully?*[1]

I first thought I would include here stories about Henri, about time we spent together, about the wildly disparate paths he travelled as a Caregiver, some of which I walked along with him. But Michelle has so exquisitely woven Henri, his life, his wonderings into this conversation, it would have been less than helpful to add my own.

The only honourable place we can possibly begin this pilgrimage together – to slowly quiet this flailing, screaming machine, generating impossible demands – is to return to our centre, bring ourselves home, and start where we are. There, we can inventory whatever we have been given: Our lives. Our presence. Our Time. Our Company. As our wisdom traditions and life lessons teach us, caring and growing in community with others is the key. When two or more gather in this way, faithful in the knowing that this, miraculously, is enough, what happens next is beyond our dominion and our imagining. We don't often know what this will look like, but we can know this much: it will surely take our breath away.

Wayne Muller
Santa Fe, New Mexico
September 2019

Introduction

C are, compassion and suffering are concepts recognized by virtually all cultures and wisdom traditions as core elements of the human condition. Yet, they each hold nuances which shine differently when viewed from various perspectives, akin to the effects noted when one holds a diamond to the light. Exercising compassion and caring for another is something most people have experience with, whether they have cradled a newborn baby, listened to the story of a friend who was distraught, or cared physically for ailing family members or friends. For those who have chosen professions in the caring realm, these concepts are particularly important, since both their personal and professional lives are impacted by how they perceive and experience care and caregiving.

In my own life, I have come to learn about providing as well as receiving care through my roles as a mother, wife, daughter, sister and friend. I have also been privileged to experience more than 40 wonderful years in the nursing profession, with a portion of those years also dedicated to theological study and pastoral care ministry. Many rich encounters of caring have formed who I am today, teaching me much about suffering as I attempt to continue working through my own understanding of caring with a compassionate heart.

And yet, time and again I have witnessed how beautiful hearts, including my own, become tired and broken when the burden of caring becomes onerous. With millions of people involved in caring professions in North America, and millions more caring for their own family and friends in an unpaid role, supporting and nourishing caregivers is a monumental but essential task. This inspirational resource has been developed to provide awareness, tools and encouragement, particularly for those engaged in formal caregiving roles. The Henri Nouwen Society is dedicated to the important work of supporting caregivers, and continues to publish and develop materials and programs for those who provide care to others, either personally or professionally.

Years ago, in my personal attempt to learn more about the nuances of care and compassion, specifically care for the dying, I was fortunate to discover the extensive writings of Henri J. M. Nouwen. Henri's words resonated with me on many levels, deeply impacting my life both personally and professionally. Accompanying those who are dying often involves exploring existential and spiritual landscapes, confronting many of life's mysteries and questions. Henri's work helped me become more comfortable exploring not only my patients' questions with them, but ultimately my own questions as well.

Nouwen lived a very full life in many different circles, until his untimely death in 1996 at the age of 64. Born in the Netherlands, he was ordained a Roman Catholic priest in 1957 and found himself involved in a progressive post-war church that was more open to the laity and focused on outreach. It was a church attempting to speak to the needs of modern people in a changing world, trying to become more inclusive and attentive. These qualities would become hallmarks of the spirituality he would teach and promote for the rest of his life.

After obtaining further education and an advanced degree in psychology, Henri moved to the United States and enrolled in a new program of studies in religion and psychiatry at the Menninger Institute in Kansas. This would become the birthplace of Clinical Pastoral Education – what modern-day chaplains and pastoral counsellors know as CPE. Henri believed that there was a deep connection between the mind and the heart, and was convinced that true care should reflect what we refer to now as "whole-person care" – the need to provide care not just for the body, but for the mind and the spirit as well.

Nouwen went on to teach at the University of Notre Dame, and in the Divinity schools at Harvard and Yale. After many years in academia, he followed the urgings of his restless heart, exploring other life experiences, including periods as a missionary in South America and time in a monastery. Eventually, he became friends with Jean Vanier, a Canadian philosopher and theologian living in France. It was there that Henri was introduced to the L'Arche movement. (This is the French word for "The Ark" – a place of refuge and safety.) Vanier initiated L'Arche in the 1960s, establishing first one home, then several, where persons with intellectual and physical disabilities could live in small communities with their caregivers (called assistants) instead of in institutions. The movement flourished; today there are more than 150 L'Arche communities in over 40 countries and on five continents. In 1986 Henri was invited to Canada and lived the final ten years of his life as a pastor at L'Arche Daybreak in Richmond Hill, Ontario.

During those years at Daybreak, Henri continued to write and teach. He spent time developing deep friendships while also providing physical and spiritual care to the "core members," as they are called, experiencing for himself the profound mutuality present in the gifts you not only give but receive while caring for another. It was also during this period that he found himself struggling with his own mental health, taking time away at one point for intense therapy to treat a profound psychological and emotional crisis. During this dark period, he kept a journal that was eventually published as *The Inner Voice of Love: A Journey through Anguish to Freedom.* It is one of his most well-loved books, appealing to people from all walks of life who relate to his pain and anguish, his depression and loss of hope.

A prolific writer, Henri went on to publish nearly 40 books during his lifetime; these have been sold internationally and translated into more than 20 languages. His books remain popular, inspiring new readers from bankers to politicians, teachers, religious leaders, seekers, activists, parents and caregivers. Writers and researchers continue to explore his literary legacy, and works associated with him continue to be published. Although Henri's formation is rooted in the Christian tradition, and his writing often reflects this perspective, his desire was to engage people of all faiths and walks of life. His background in spirituality and psychology, along with his rich lived experience, allowed him to provide insights and language that bridged the sacred and the secular, appealing to wide and varied audiences.

Healthy Caregiving features not only Nouwen's work, but also the work of other experts in various fields. It is filled with caregiving stories, where sometimes the names have been changed to maintain the confidentiality of the person's identity. The self-reflective questions at the end of each section encourage the reader to explore their own care experiences and inner landscape to find support and nourishment for their caregiving journey. As you move through this resource, Henri's perennial wisdom is apparent; it lays a firm foundation that originates from the understanding that "caring is the privilege of every person and is at the heart of being human."[1]

1

The Call to Care

*Caring is the privilege of every person
and is at the heart of being human.*

Henri Nouwen

Perspectives on Care and Compassion

Although all of us would like to believe that we are people who care, our society tends to use the word "care" in many ambiguous and indifferent ways. "Do you want a coffee?" "I don't care." Or, "Who will look after the house while I'm gone?" "I'll take care of it." We can also care *about* something or someone, which is different than caring *for* someone and actually addressing their needs. Most of us have experienced caring for someone's needs at some point in our lives. We can appreciate that in many respects, caring for another is a universal experience in human life. People often provide care for others in more informal or unpaid caregiving roles – parents caring for children, children caring for aging parents, loved ones caring for family or friends who are ill, or spouses caring for one another as they age. Caregivers in these instances usually find that this is not something they necessarily chose to do; they can feel overwhelmed and unprepared for what they are undertaking. It is sometimes referred to as the "unchosen profession."

For those engaged in an occupation or a more formal role tied to caring for others, the word "care" takes on different understandings or perspectives. A professional caregiver would normally be hired or engaged by an organization to use their skills and insights to address a client's needs and to take "care" of them. Whether they are involved in health care, social services, teaching or ministry, or have trained and engaged in a care sector as a volunteer, it is easy for this more formal caregiver role to be understood as something functional or practical. Basically, someone has a need and the care provider offers a skill or a service to meet that need, providing medical care, physical care, counselling or support, to name a few.

Understanding care solely from a service perspective can consciously or unconsciously foster an attitude of power between those providing care and those receiving care. The care provider viewpoint, put simply, would be "I have something that you need." Their sense of power may not be intentional, but each care encounter runs the risk of creating the type of perception associated with "I am strong and you are weak"; "I am healthy and you are sick and vulnerable"; "I am powerful and you are powerless."

Yet, many of us involved in caring professions believe that the care we offer is more than providing a service. We also desire to offer comfort, encouragement and a personal touch as we engage with those who require our expertise. Henri Nouwen would agree that true care is not ambiguous, or indifferent, and is not tied solely to service. His writings go even further to invite us to consider looking at the word "care" and our response to suffering from a perspective we may not have considered.

> The word care finds its roots in the Gothic *Kara*, which means lament. The basic meaning of care is "to grieve, to experience sorrow, to cry out with." I am very much struck by this background of the word care because we tend to look at caring as an attitude of the strong toward

the weak, of the powerful toward the powerless, of the haves toward the have-nots. And, in fact, we feel quite uncomfortable with an invitation to enter into someone's pain before doing something about it.[1]

When I first reflected on this definition, it was a new concept for me. Working for many years as an emergency room nurse, I was very focused on "fixing" things for people or using my skills to assess their needs and triaging them to have their acute physical or psychological problems taken care of efficiently and effectively. I was never invited to consider "entering into someone else's pain before doing something about it." Although I believe I had empathy for others and tried to treat people with compassion, I had not consciously thought about entering into their pain before attempting to "fix" it.

Later in my career, as the coordinator of a residential hospice, I became convinced that this kind of approach to care was invaluable. Working with palliative care providers at our local hospital and those caring for people at home, part of my role was to determine the appropriate time to offer someone admission to our residence.

Fred was a very independent man who truly wanted to remain at home to die, but his family needed respite not only from his physical care but also his tendency to be stubborn on a number of fronts. One day, the community nurse called me to see if we had a bed. After weeks of coaxing, she had finally caught Fred in a weak moment and he conceded to come to hospice. His family was so relieved! Shortly after his arrival, the staff came to me and asked me to speak with him and his family. Apparently, he was bent on leaving already!

Upon entering his suite, I found him fully clothed, sitting up straight in bed, with an exasperated look on his face. I sat down beside the bed with his wife and daughter and introduced myself to everyone. Instead of beginning by trying to convince him to stay, I wanted to find out more about Fred and why he didn't want to be at hospice. I listened as he explained, "If you think I am just going to sit in this room and stare at these walls until I die, you've got another thing coming." The tears in the eyes of his wife and daughter and the looks on their faces cued me into their conflicting feelings: their love for him, their embarrassment at his candour, and their definite need for a break from caregiving.

What he shared with me shaped my response. "Fred, I have a secret to tell you. Hospice care is not really about dying – it is all about living. We don't want you to sit in this room staring at the walls until you die. This is your home now, and you can live here the same way you would live at home. You have a fridge here to keep whatever you like to eat or drink, your friends and family can come and go anytime they wish, and you are free to transform this room to your own liking and use the whole facility as much as you want to. Nobody knows if you have two weeks or two months or more to live, but however long that time is, we are here to keep you comfortable and well so you can do the best living you can with the time you have left." He seemed to soften with these words, and over the next while, as we got to know Fred, we were able to help him to not just live but to thrive – so much so that he was able to be temporarily discharged home for a short while when his condition plateaued.

Our spiritual care coordinator, Bridget, spent lots of time getting to know the residents and their families, including their hobbies, likes, dislikes, fears, questions and more. Bridget and the staff found out two things about Fred: one, that he was a serious Toronto Maple Leafs hockey fan, and two, that he loved building and racing remote-control cars. With the encouragement of one of our personal support workers (PSWs), Fred's family transformed his room into a Maple Leafs shrine, surrounding him with things from home that made him feel comfortable. Hockey games on his flat screen TV were special events! He also was able to convert the sofa in his suite into a workbench of sorts, laden with tools and car parts as he worked away on the hobby he loved. It was great fun to watch his cars racing down the hallway of the hospice!

Henri Nouwen's invitation to enter into someone else's pain before addressing it encourages us to be present to that person

– fully present to them – with our intellect and our skills as '
as our heart, our time and our listening ears. We are encouraged to respond to the one who is suffering by recognizing their
situation and stopping to consciously "be" with them, before we
"do" anything about it. This is not so much about the amount
of time we spend as it is about our attitude, the way we engage
them, and the way we respond to what they *truly* need beyond
the obvious. Although our natural impulse might be to begin
our care encounter with a more intellectual problem-solving
response, Henri asks us to take even a moment and first respond
with who we are, not just what we know: one person to another,
equals in our shared humanity and vulnerability. As I reflect on
entering Fred's room for the first time, I recall that I was afraid
that I would not know how to convince him to stay. Allowing
him to speak his truth instead of dismissing it, and attending to
his fears and frustrations, helped us to establish our relationship
with Fred and his family on a good footing.

This type of response relates to how Henri would describe
compassion. "The word *compassion* is derived from the Latin
words *pati* and *cum*, which together mean 'to suffer with.'
Compassion asks us to go where it hurts, to enter into places
of pain, to share in brokenness, fear, confusion, and anguish…
Compassion means full immersion in the condition of being
human."[2] Compassion invites us to become vulnerable ourselves,
and to come close to the one who suffers. We can respond
that way only when the other ceases to be "someone else" and
becomes like us. We find it is easier to show pity than compassion, because the suffering person calls us to be aware of our
own suffering.

Shane Sinclair and his colleagues published an article in
Palliative Medicine in 2017 that reflected data collected on palliative care patients and their understandings and experiences of
three elements offered by their health care providers: sympathy,
empathy and compassion. It noted how these related constructs
are often used interchangeably within the health care literature,
despite some notable differences.

The relationship between sympathy, empathy, and compassion.

	SYMPATHY	EMPATHY	COMPASSION
Definition	A pity-based response to a distressing situation that is characterized by a lack of relational understanding and the self-preservation of the observer	An affective response that acknowledges and attempts to understand an individual's suffering through emotional resonance	A virtuous response that seeks to address the suffering and needs of a person through relational understanding and action
Defining characteristics	Observing/Reacting/Misguided Lack of understanding Unhelpful Ego based Self-preservation	Acknowledgement of suffering Understanding the person Affective response	Supererogatory Non-conditional/Virtuous Altruistic/Instrumental Action-oriented response
Response to suffering	Acknowledgement	Acknowledgement, understanding and emotional resonance	Acknowledgement, understanding, and emotional resonance linked with action aimed at understanding the person and the amelioration of suffering
Type of response	A visceral reaction to a distressing situation	An objective and affective response to a distressing situation	A proactive and targeted response to a distressing situation

Emotional state of observer	Emotional dissonance	Emotional resonance and emotional contagion ("feeling with")	Emotional engagement and resilience
Motivators of response	Pity/ego/obligation	Circumstantial/affective state of observer/duty/relatedness to patient/deservedness of patient	Virtues/dispositional
Relationship of observer to suffering	External	Proximal/isomorphic	Instrumental/relational/transmorphic
Intended outcomes	Self-preservation of observer	Objective and affective understanding of sufferer	Amelioration of multifactorial suffering
Patient-reported outcomes	Demoralized/Patronized Overwhelmed Compounded suffering	Heard/Understood Validated	Relief of suffering Enhanced sense of well-being Enhanced quality of caregiving
Examples	"I'm so sorry" "This must be awful" "I can't imagine what it must be like"	"Help me to understand your situation" "I get the sense that you are feeling …" "I feel your sadness"	"I know you are suffering, but are there things I can do to help it be better?" "What can I do to improve your situation?"

Shane Sinclair et al., Sympathy, Empathy and Compassion: A Grounded Theory Study of Palliative Care Patients' Understandings, Experiences, and Preferences, *Palliative Medicine* 31:5 (2017), 442.

In the preceding chart, we see the subtle but important differences not only in the definitions, but also in the response motivators as well as the patient-reported outcomes. Sympathy, perceived as an unwanted pity-based response, had a largely detrimental effect on patient well-being. Instead of having a healing effect, sympathy often left the care receivers feeling demoralized, depressed and sorry for themselves. Providers offering more empathic responses left the patients feeling more understood and validated, but the ones providing a compassionate response seemed to assist more in relieving suffering and enhancing a sense of well-being. One patient in particular described empathy and compassion this way: "I think empathy is more of a feeling thing where you're aware of somebody's suffering, and compassion is when you act on that knowledge."[3]

In our task-oriented society, with health care and social service systems focused on streamlining services, it might seem difficult, if not impossible, to be able to offer truly compassionate care to the people we support. Trying to attend to the care of the whole person in light of the constraints of time and the boundaries of the therapeutic relationship is not always easy. It is hoped that the material you find in this resource will nourish and support you as you attempt to become more aware of this type of care and how you might offer it to others and to yourself.

Questions for Reflection

1. Are these definitions of care and compassion that Nouwen uses new for you? In what ways?

2. What is it like for you to care about someone or something? To be there in that situation?

3. When does it feel good to care? When does it not feel good to care?

4. What differences do you notice when you look at Sinclair's comparisons of sympathy, empathy and compassion? Which one do you see yourself working out of for the most part? Does the patient/client experience of these surprise you?

5. When you engage with a client/patient/resident, do you
   try to discover what their needs are, beyond the obvious?
   How do you do that? How can you expand what you do
   to accomplish this more often?

Care versus Cure

Another perspective that Henri invites us to reflect on is the
difference between care and cure. In a culture and a health care
system focused on cure, it can be difficult to know what to say
to people who are living with life-limiting or life-threatening
diseases, advanced dementia, or chronic diseases with lifelong
challenges. This reality is also faced by many people living with
disabilities who are not seeking a cure or a change to their bodies, and do not see their lives as particularly filled with pain and
suffering. Their abilities are part of their identity. The changes
they desire do not revolve around a cure; instead, they focus on
removing the barriers inherent in our society that affect attitude,
access, communication and more.

Henri understood that the ability to care for one another
was a universal gift of being human, and believed that care and
compassion were always able to be shared, even when a cure
was not possible. We often hear of the person who has been
told by their specialist that there is no more treatment available
for their disease – that there is "nothing more we can do." The
truth is, at this moment, there is usually much more that can be
done. This is exactly the time when we can offer a tremendous
amount of care and compassion, despite the fact that a cure is
not on the horizon.

Being able to cure, at its foundation, is born out of a desire
to relieve suffering and restore the person to a greater state of
health. We are all happy when we hear that someone has been
cured of their disease or condition. However, the desire to cure
can keep us focused on "success," which can build a sense of
power and prestige in some people and a sense of loss or defeat
in those who do not experience that outcome. When people
finish their sessions of chemo or radiation, we often applaud

as they ring the bell or the gong at the cancer centre to indicate their final treatment. Yet, how does that impact those who are in the cancer suite, undergoing treatment that will not end before they die? How does it make them feel to hear that bell if they know their own disease is not curable?

In cancer care especially, we also tend to focus on using "battle" language, encouraging people to "fight" their disease. Those who will die from their cancer can be left feeling like they were a failure because they didn't fight hard enough. "If I had enough faith or enough willpower, I would have made it. I am so sorry I let you down." Some don't want to be remembered as "losing a brave fight" against cancer, and would rather be remembered for how they made a difference in the world. Others don't want to be defined by their cancer: that they "conquered it" or that they are a "survivor." Yet, some find this language helpful and comforting. Each person is different, and it is important to engage them in conversations about their own wishes and comfort regarding language around their disease, instead of assuming we know what they want or need. This is another way we enter into their pain before naming it or addressing it.

The ability to focus on care above the need to cure helps us to see the person first, instead of the disease or disability. It gives us the opportunity to learn from them and their experiences, and can help us to become more comfortable with our own aging, weakness and dying. As we accompany those who teach us these important life lessons, we often discover that both parties experience growth and healing. This is a true gift. When our response to another person's suffering can be more about being with them before doing something about it, we learn that our very presence is often enough to bring healing to that situation.

Still, when we honestly ask ourselves which persons in our lives mean the most to us, we often find that it is those who, instead of giving much advice, solutions, or cures, have chosen rather to share our pain and touch our wounds with a gentle and tender hand. The friend who can be silent with us in a moment of despair or confusion, who can stay with us in an hour of grief and bereavement, who can tolerate not-knowing, not-curing, not-healing and face with us the reality of our powerlessness, that is the friend who cares.[4]

In our professional circles, we have been taught to maintain a professional distance from the person seeking care. This may make us nervous or unsure about Nouwen's understanding of care, which asks us to be more intentional, wholistic and even vulnerable with how we respond to those we care for every day. Mike Martin, who writes about professional ethics, explains that professionals can be criticized for being too detached, but also for not having enough distance. "Professional responsibilities do call for some forms of distance that limit the expression of personal values in professional life. Distance does not, however, imply the absence of caring and personal involvement. On the contrary, limited detachment often promotes ideals of caring that are simultaneously personal and professional."[5]

Henri struggled early in his professional life with finding this balance in caring for the other. His background in psychology and his training in the new field of Clinical Pastoral Education focused on the clinical and academic aspects of this work. Yet, a large body of his writing addressed what he felt was the overprofessionalization of caring and the need to transcend the temptation of too much distance, focusing on the essence of the person through ministry and compassion. His books *Compassion* and *The Wounded Healer* were just two of many that referred to the need to care deeply for the whole person, at the same time recognizing our own needs and brokenness as we walk in human solidarity with those we are called to care for or serve. For decades, Henri became an important guide in humanizing care. I believe his words remain true today as we seek to address the more mechanical, industrial model of care we have adopted as we institutionalized our systems and developed metrics that reflect impact and production instead of the uniqueness and dignity of each human person we care for.

Questions for Reflection

1. Recall a caregiving experience where you have been faced with care that was not related to cure. What elements do you remember? What did you learn about the difference between care and cure?

2. What are some of the struggles you face in providing this kind of care to others?

3. What are your thoughts on the language or rituals we use sometimes to promote cure? Does this impact how you provide care?

4. Does the language influence how you communicate with other clients and other professionals involved in their care/services?

Care: Our Response to Suffering

Helen Keller, a woman whose early illness left her deaf and blind, knew suffering intimately. She is credited with saying that "although the world is full of suffering, it is full also of the overcoming of it." This wisdom gives us hope and a sense that we all have the capacity to respond to another person's pain with some ability to help them towards healing.

Dr. Eric Cassell, in *The Nature of Suffering and the Goals of Medicine*, defined suffering as "the state of severe distress associated with events that threaten the intactness of the person."[6] All the aspects of personhood – the lived past, the family's lived past, culture and society, roles, the instrumental dimension, associations and relationships, the body, the unconscious mind, the political being, the secret life, the perceived future and the transcendent dimension – are susceptible to damage and loss. Cassell concludes that transcendence is probably the most powerful way in which one is restored to wholeness after an injury to personhood. When experienced, transcendence locates the person in a far larger landscape where the sufferer is no longer isolated by pain but is brought closer to a transpersonal source of meaning and to a human community that shares those

meanings. In other words, sharing our suffering with ot
takes it out of its isolation and can move us to healing. Henri
reminds us of this and encourages our caring through the gift
of true presence and sharing.

> So much of our suffering arises not just out of our pain-
> ful condition, but from our feeling of isolation in the
> midst of our pain. Many people who suffer immensely
> from addiction … find their first real relief when they
> can share their pain with others and discover that they
> are truly heard. The many twelve-step programs are a
> powerful witness to the truth that sharing our pain is the
> beginning of healing. Here we can see how close sorrow
> and joy can be. When I discover that I am no longer
> alone in my struggle and when I start experiencing a
> new "fellowship in weakness," then true joy can erupt,
> right in the middle of my sorrow.[7]

This "fellowship in weakness" that Henri talks about reminds
us that part of being human means that we all experience our
own personal vulnerabilities and suffering. Although professional caregivers should never overtly share their personal suffering with those they care for, these experiences remain a part
of the self that we bring to any care relationship. It is important
for those who provide care to learn how to name their own fears
and feelings, and reflect on their stories of caregiving to grow
personally and professionally, working through the emotions
that surface as they care for others. This inner work will also help
caregivers to be more comfortable speaking with care recipients
and families about their feelings and their suffering. Susan is
a spiritual care provider who works with a community agency
to support clients and their families as well as the care team
members. She explains that whenever she is doing orientation
with new front-line staff, she urges them to reflect on the reality
that the only thing separating them from those they care for is
a diagnosis. Our own lives as caregivers can often run in paral-
lel streams to those we care for. We must work hard at coming

to terms with our own emotions and experiences so we can be effective as we journey with others.

Learning how to speak with those who are suffering is an art that caregivers must continuously develop. In her book *Suffering and Spirituality*, nurse educator Lorraine M. Wright explains that for the most part, changing societal beliefs in North America seem to value the pursuit of happiness and the avoidance of suffering. "Instead of inquiring about illness suffering, healthcare professionals tend to use more upbeat and positive language with questions such as 'How are you coping with your illness?' or 'How are you adjusting?' ... As one young man said to me during our therapeutic conversations together when we discussed his suffering from chronic pain, 'At last someone is calling it what it is. I *do* suffer; it saps my spirit and I am tired of hearing how well I am coping.'"[8]

Speaking openly about suffering is difficult. As carers, as much as we want to be able to eradicate it, we often realize we are woefully inadequate at doing so. For the most part, besides avoiding the language or topic of suffering, we tend to equate suffering with physical pain. Suffering is so much more than that: it includes a larger realm of mental, emotional or spiritual pain or any unpleasant feeling, emotion or sensation. It can manifest itself as physical pain, depression or anxiety, social isolation, or spiritual or existential distress. Even physical pain is multidimensional and may be worsened or perhaps relieved if attention is given to the other dimensions of the person's suffering. Some studies suggest that existential and spiritual issues may be of greater concern to patients than physical pain and symptoms. The founder of modern palliative care, Dame Cicely Saunders, introduced the concept of "total pain," which may include one or all of these elements.

There is not only one way to alleviate suffering, nor can it ever be completely alleviated. There will always be suffering of some kind, for it is a part of the human condition. Our tendency in the health care system has been to medicalize suffering, addressing it as something that can be cured or healed with the right medication or treatment. Naming the emotions and experiences of those who are suffering can be validating and even transforming for both the provider and the care recipient.

Everyone's suffering is unique and personal. We can never assume that two people suffer the same way or that their suffering can be equated with ours. Nouwen reminds us of the danger of comparing suffering, and how that can affect the healing that takes place. "I am deeply convinced that each human being suffers in a way no other human being suffers…. In the final analysis, your pain and my pain are so deeply personal that comparing them can bring scarcely any consolation or comfort."[9]

As Wright explains, suffering can heal and change us – care receivers as well as care providers.

> Suffering does change us, and often for the better. Frequently, we have a deepened compassion, a more tender heart, or become less judgemental. But, suffering can also invite bitterness over losses, confusion about life's abrupt changes, anger over what might have been, and even competitiveness over what type of suffering is the most severe. These varying responses to suffering are all based on the stories we have created from our particular illness beliefs.[10]

Nouwen offers another important perspective about suffering. Some people, according to their culture, stories, beliefs or faith tradition, may believe that God has caused their suffering or that it is happening because they need to be punished. This can bring a great amount of spiritual distress to the situation. Henri, speaking from his Catholic Christian tradition, addresses this point in a way that may assist people in their suffering.

> We are often tempted to "explain" suffering in terms of "the will of God." Not only can this evoke anger and frustration, but also it is false. "God's will" is not a label that can be put on unhappy situations. God wants to bring joy not pain, peace not war, healing not suffering. Therefore, instead of declaring anything and everything

e the will of God, we must be willing to ask ourselves where in the midst of our pains and sufferings we can discern the loving presence of God.[11]

Our compassionate and caring response of presence and active listening when suffering is revealed is at the heart of how we begin to bring healing and hope to those we care for.

Questions for Reflection

1. Recall a time when you found yourself caring for someone who was suffering deeply. How did you feel about your ability to address their needs? What might you do differently if you cared for them today?

2. Looking back on that encounter, what did you learn about suffering?

3. What did you learn about yourself? How has this changed you?

Reflecting on Our Stories

Vivianne recalls the story of a grandfather she cared for as a community nurse many years ago. She marvels at how many things she learned about caring and about herself from this one patient and his family. Ken had a large odorous wound on the stump of his amputated leg. He was becoming very weak from his cancer, and knew that his time was limited. Although the nursing focus was his wound care, his suffering arose from the fact that he could no longer go down the stairs in his home. His workshop was downstairs, and he had promised his six-year-old granddaughter that he would finish building a dollhouse for her as a final gift. With only weeks to live, he was devastated and depressed that he could not grant her wish.

Vivianne and Ken's wife put their heads together. They contacted friends who brought tools and set up a workshop on the kitchen table. Since Ken was open to receiving help with the project, he was able to put the finishing touches on the dollhouse while he still had the strength. Reflecting on this story, Vivianne marvels at what she learned about legacy, sacrifice, resilience and being open to allowing help from others. A nursing colleague gave a wonderful gift to her, teaching her how to manage the odour from Ken's wound so that he could experience dignity and comfort when his friends came by to help with the dollhouse. The ripple effect was seeing how his friends extended this same dignity to him. At first, their visits included joking around with Ken and keeping the conversation light. Eventually, however, they were able to support their buddy emotionally as they began to feel more comfortable talking about serious issues with Ken, including his dying.

Vivianne remarks that Ken's wife taught her many things. One indelible lesson was about true love and sacrifice, as she was willing to let so many strangers into their home to make Ken's last days memorable. So many lessons, and so many powerful reflections, from one story of care.

Stories are essential to our understanding of human life. They help us to make sense of the narrative of our own lives and the lives of others. Much of what we have learned throughout our lives has been transmitted through stories told to us by our parents, teachers, family members and friends. The most powerful human stories keep working in our hearts over time; some become beacons of light for a lifetime. Stories can touch hearts across the street or across the globe. We may remember the story of the young soccer players and their coach trapped in a cave in Thailand, as the entire world waited with fear and anticipation for days, praying for rescuers to find a way to free them before monsoon rains sealed their exit and their fate. Or we may recall stories of people who have been missing or held hostage, finally found safe after long periods of time. What we learn about fear, courage, love and hope from these situations can sustain us in our own times of doubt and difficulty.

Our personal stories are important for our own self-understanding and can become a light for others as well. Marjorie Thompson explains in *Courage for Caregivers* that our stories can communicate who we are, how we mature and how we connect. To tell a story requires some measure of reflection, which helps us not to miss the lesson to be learned as our lives unfold. In sharing stories, we piece together the sequence of events, our felt experience and the recollections of others who were part of the situation.

As we do this, a frame of meaning often emerges that gives the story cohesion. Sometimes we carry the meaning in a narrative – a word picture of unfolding events, characters involved and fragments of dialogue. Sometimes we express the meaning in terms of insight, wisdom, depth of emotion or spiritual growth. A sense of meaning or higher purpose in the stories of our lives can come through reflection on our experiences over time. Marjorie reminds us that the lens of another person's story may help us to see a larger picture in our circumstances. Stories can help us to surface emotions and memories that were buried or supressed, which can lead to healing as we share and work through them.[12]

Henri Nouwen was a prolific writer and storyteller. Some of his best-loved books were diaries he kept about his travels and encounters in Guatemala, at the Genessee Abbey, and during the one-year sabbatical he took before he died. As he put it, "My hope is that the description of God's love in my life will give you the freedom and courage to discover – and maybe also describe – God's love in yours."[13] Nouwen's firm belief was that sharing our experiences as well as our vulnerabilities and weaknesses helps to make us whole and serves to heal our own wounds and the wounds of others.

We all come from different lives and roles, different care settings and experiences. Our caregiving is often a combination of the professional and the personal, including caring for our families, friends and neighbours. As Nouwen believed, there is a clear connection between our hearts and our minds. Examining our lived experiences and stories in light of our values and struggles can truly help us to grow both personally and professionally.

Questions for Reflection

1. Recall a caregiving story where you learned something about yourself.
2. Find someone to share a caregiving story with out loud. Many times, there are more lessons to be learned in the telling of the story than simply reflecting on it privately.
3. Do you take time regularly to reflect on your care stories? Do you see the value in this? If you have not made a habit of reflecting on your care stories, what can you do to work that into your life and schedule?

Caregiving as Vocation

Life as a caregiver is not always a choice. Unpaid caregivers may find themselves caring for the needs of their loved ones for a long time – perhaps even a lifetime. The Henri Nouwen Society resource *Courage for Caregivers* is designed to support those who provide care to a family member or friend. More information on this resource can be found at www.henrinouwen.org.

However, many people do make conscious choices to be part of a profession or a role which supports others on a daily basis. They may care for hundreds or even thousands of people over their working life. This type of work, focused on caring for many people at a time who are not connected personally to the provider, can pose its own set of challenges. Facing these challenges, trying to maintain professionalism and expertise, and striving to provide the type of care Henri speaks of can be difficult.

People choose to work in a caregiving field for any number of reasons. Perhaps they have been touched by a particular life circumstance. I have a number of friends who went into nursing or medicine because their parents faced a diagnosis of cancer or another disease. Sometimes people follow in the footsteps of their parents or teachers; they choose a career in a care sector because they have witnessed joy or fulfillment in those who raised or mentored them. There are obviously many reasons to choose this path.

Poet Mary Oliver puts it to us candidly in her poem "The Summer Day": "Tell me, what is it you plan to do with your one wild and precious life?" When our life is wide open before us, there seem to be countless possibilities. Even if we have been engaged in our profession for a while, it is good to sit back and reflect. Are we happy doing what we are doing? Is it fulfilling? I always like to invite people to consider this question: "Is what you are doing life-giving or life-draining?" Sometimes there are elements of both. Self-reflective practice is important in caregiving, personally and professionally. We will keep coming back to this concept and explore different ways in which it can help us to grow and transform. A good place to begin is by regularly looking in the mirror. A friend of mine once said something that I believe rings true for many: "For the past 33 years, I have looked in the mirror every morning and asked myself: 'If today were the last day of my life, would I want to do what I am about to do today?' And whenever the answer has been 'No' for too many days in a row, I know I need to change something."

Take some time to reflect on your own story of how you came to be involved in a caregiving profession. Things have no doubt changed over time – perhaps both your work and your motivation. Viktor Frankl, an Austrian psychologist and Holocaust survivor, is quoted as saying, "Man's main concern is not to gain pleasure or to avoid pain but rather to see a meaning in his life."[14] It may benefit you to look at your own situation in light of some of the research being done on job meaning and whether you believe you are engaged in a job, a career or a calling.

Dr. Amy Wrzesniewski, a professor at the Yale School of Management, has spent her career researching how individuals identify with their work. Her paper "On the Meaning of Work: A Theoretical Integration and Review," written with Brent Rosso and Kathryn Dekas, talks about some of the literature

they reviewed that supported placing the sources of '
for one's work into four different categories:

1. **Self** – How do the person's values, motivations and beliefs connect with their work to give it meaning?

2. **Others** – Colleagues such as co-workers, managers, other groups and outside communities, including a person's family, can inform the kind of meaning they make of our work.

3. **Work context** – How is the job designed? What is the mission of the organization? What is happening in the national culture related to this kind of work?

4. **Spirituality** – There seems to be a fundamental need for meaning that can ground itself in one's own understanding of self in light of one's spirituality – their aspiration toward a connection to the sacred, including a higher power, guiding force or energy, or belief system.[15]

The writers felt that there needed to be more research done in area number four, where people find meaning in their work from a spiritual perspective. They agreed that this could be difficult to measure or assess, but thought researchers could look at the intersection of psychology and organizational behaviour and how work helps us to transcend the self (as described in Maslow's hierarchy of needs, with a top level of self-actualization or self-transcendence). It was noted that although they may be reluctant to discuss it at work, large numbers of employees across the world think of their work in spiritual terms and see their beliefs, culture or religion playing an important role in how they conduct their work lives. This suggests that a person's spiritual life has an important influence on the meaning of their work, yet is often overlooked in organizational scholarship.[16]

This ties in with the concept of "vocation," which is usually connected to a more religious context. The word "vocation" has its roots in the Latin word *vocare*, which means "call." Historically, this referred to a sacred calling from God to a particular vocation in life. In current literature, it refers to the work we do being a contribution to the world, to the greater good, beyond the self, and sees that as part of self-transcendence. The ancient Greek philosopher Aristotle is thought to have coined the phrase "Where the needs of the world and your talents cross, there lies your *vocation*." Spiritual writer Frederick Buechner expressed it with these words: "The place God calls you to is the place where your deep gladness and the world's deep hunger meet."[17]

Wrzeniewski's research also focuses on how people see themselves orientated to their work, which can determine the meaning they find in their employment and in turn affect their level of job satisfaction. These categories include seeing one's work as a job, a career or a calling. She has found that in most instances, a similar number of people in each organization come from each of these three categories, and that you can move between them with a change of mindset. She also cautions that no category of work orientation is more legitimate than the others: each is a valid way to approach your professional life.

1. **Job** – These employees view their job as a means to an end, working for pay and benefits to support their families, hobbies and life outside of work. They prefer jobs that do not interfere with their personal lives, and likely don't have a strong connection to the workplace.

2. **Career** – If a job is something you do for someone else, a career is something you do for yourself. The focus is on moving upward, acquiring success, receiving raises and new titles which can assist in better pay, more satisfaction, and a higher social standing.

3. **Calling** – Individuals with a calling orientation describe their work as integral to their lives and their identity. They view their career as a form of self-expression and personal fulfillment. They are more likely to find their work meaningful and will modify their duties and develop relationships to make it more so. They are found to be more satisfied in general with their work and their lives.[18]

This information begs us to ask ourselves which category we find ourselves in at this time in our lives, and if we have found or continue to find meaning in our work. As caregivers, our roles can be more complicated, since they involve the care for a particular element of someone else's life. Finding meaning there can help us to build resilience and a firm foundation for a healthy and fulfilling work life.

Many wisdom traditions speak to this element of paying attention to the viewpoint of care and compassion and the orientation we are coming from as we move through our day. Thich Nhat Hanh, the beloved Buddhist monk, encourages us with this verse:

Waking up this morning, I smile.
Twenty-four brand new hours are before me.
I vow to live fully in each moment
and to look at all beings with eyes of compassion.[19]

When we speak of our vocation from an interior or spiritual perspective, we might use the word "discernment" to describe the soul-searching we do to discover what our heart and perhaps our God is trying to tell us about where we are being called in our life and our work. Parker Palmer, a writer from the Quaker tradition and good friend of Henri's, has written much about letting your life speak, and how connected your soul and your role are. Later in his life, Parker reflected on some of the things he learned through time and experience to understand his own vocation. When he was younger, he believed that it was his responsibility to conjure the highest values he could find and then conform his life to them. His heroes included people with great moral standards – Martin Luther King Jr., Rosa Parks, Mahatma Gandhi and Dorothy Day – which set the bar very high. He realized the hard way that although it was admirable to try to live up to the lofty ideals of others, he ended up living a way of life that was not his own. His advice now, after experiencing both success and failure at living out of his true self, is to take time to listen to your life and explore your values, instead of telling your life what you would like to accomplish.

As we close this chapter on our Call to Care, Henri's wisdom can help us look at our own caregiving role(s) at this time in our life and give us some perspectives for our own further reflection.

Often we want to be somewhere other than where we are, or even to be someone other than who we are. We tend to compare ourselves constantly with others and wonder why we are not as rich, as intelligent, as simple, as generous, or as saintly as they are. Such comparisons make us feel guilty, ashamed, or jealous. It is very important to realize that our vocation is hidden in where we are and who we are. We are unique human beings, each with a call to realize in life what nobody else can, and to realize it in the concrete context of the here and now.

We will never find our vocations by trying to figure out whether we are better or worse than others. We are good enough to do what we are called to do. Be yourself![20]

We are not called to save the world, solve all problems, and help all people. But each of us has our own unique call, in our families, in our work and in our world.[21]

For Henri Nouwen, *spiritual discernment* is hearing a deeper sound beneath the noise of ordinary life and seeing through appearances to the *interconnectedness* of all things, to gain a vision of how things hang together in our lives and in the world.[22] As long as we believe that our pains and struggles connect us with our fellow men and women and thus make us part of the common human struggle for a better future, we are willing to accept a demanding task.[23] In a world so torn apart by rivalry, anger and hatred, we have the privileged vocation to be living signs of a love that can bridge all divisions and heal all wounds.[24] Only by attending constantly to the inner voice can you be converted to a new life of freedom and joy.[25]

2

The Mutuality
of Caregiving

*There is probably no clearer sign of true compassion
than this mutuality of giving and receiving.*

Henri Nouwen

In the professional caregiver relationship, it is understood
that there is an obligation for the caregiver to provide care
without an expectation for the care receiver to reciprocate.
It is also understood that there is an inherent power component
in this relationship. Something we don't tend to reflect on as
professional carers is that there is often a natural give and take
in the caring relationship – a mutuality where those who see
themselves as the caregiver receive something in return from
the person receiving their care.

Each care encounter has the potential to transform either
party. When I speak to groups of professional care providers,
I often ask them, "How many of you have been changed by the
people you have cared for?" Invariably, most will raise their
hands as I raise my own. What we have so often learned about
courage, suffering, dignity and even love, we have learned from
those who have allowed us the privilege of accompanying them.

In his book *Heal Thy Self: Lessons on Mindfulness in Medicine*, Saki Santorelli points out that "For too long care has been conceived of as either practitioner-centered or patient-centered. In actuality, the healing relationship has always been a crucible for mutual transformation."[1] Henri Nouwen described this mutuality of giving and receiving as one of the most beautiful characteristics of the compassionate life. "Those who have worked with the dying in Calcutta, ... who have dedicated themselves to AIDS patients or mentally handicapped people – they all will express deep gratitude for the gifts received from those they came to help. There is probably no clearer sign of true compassion than this mutuality of giving and receiving."[2]

The ten-bed residential hospice project where I worked was very dear to my heart. I had been chosen to be a part of its design, construction and opening, and the project pulled together many aspects of my personal and professional life. Seeing it come to life was truly a wonderful culmination of my nursing career. It also turned out to be a very personal project: little did I know that my own father would move in and die there two months after we opened the doors. I will share more of that precious story throughout the book.

One lesson of the mutuality of care that affected me greatly came after my father died. My dad spent his final few weeks of life living in Suite One at our hospice. It was a room where our large group of family and friends gathered frequently during those special days. After he died, I didn't realize how deeply I would suffer because of my own grief. After all, I had worked with the dying and their families for many years, and somehow I believed it would be easier for me. Yet, it certainly was a different story when it was a man I loved so much who breathed his last. Once I returned to work after the funeral, I wore a brave face and kept going. It was very difficult for me to enter Suite One, and I avoided it as much as I could.

A few months later, I reconnected with my distant cousin Walt. Walt and I didn't see one another often growing up, and hadn't been in touch for years, but when he became very ill,

I went to visit him in hospital. Part of my role with the hospital Palliative Care Department was to speak to patients about their wishes, including where they wanted to die. I saw Walt a few times during his hospital stay, and offered him the opportunity to move to hospice if he wished. He was adamant that he wanted to die at home. Although the care team and his wife felt differently, we respected his wishes.

As his illness progressed, and his care at home was more difficult to manage, Walt conceded and came to live at hospice. For some reason, I believe he was providentially placed in our only empty room at the time: Suite One. I forced myself to walk down that hallway often to spend time with him and his family, and eventually I was able to be healed of my own pain and anxiety around entering that hallowed suite that held so many memories for me. As I cared for Walt, he was not aware of it, but he also cared for me. Through his presence, and the gift of mutuality, I was able to experience my own healing and make another step forward in my journey of grief.

Healing and Wholeness

The notion of healing, especially in the health care sector, is most often equated to the physical realm: the desire to help someone be healed or cured of their disease or infirmity. It can be very focused on one wound or one facet of the person's health – helping someone to heal physically or emotionally to return to a prior state of wellness. However, if we truly wish to look at wholistic or whole-person care, we must consider exploring the healing that takes place not only in the body, but in the mind and spirit as well. Facilitating this kind of healing can be daunting for anyone providing care. It can seem impossible to accomplish with the limited scope, resources and amount of time care providers have.

The World Health Organization defines health as a "state of complete physical, mental, and social well being, and not merely the absence of disease or infirmity."[3] Many who consider themselves fairly healthy might also admit that they are living with some kind of chronic ailment, or perhaps are suffering mentally or emotionally, recognizing that their lives need healing on some level.

Healing can happen when the person feels truly cared for, listened to and less broken than when they met us. This type of healing can be extraordinary, yet it usually takes place in ordinary circumstances of care that include true presence and compassion. Dr. Rachel Naomi Remen offers us some insight into how this takes place.

> People have been healing each other since the beginning. Long before there were surgeons, psychologists, oncologists, and internists, we were there for each other.

> The healing of our present woundedness may lie in recognizing and reclaiming the capacity we all have to heal each other, the enormous power in the simplest of human relationships: the strength of a touch, the blessing of forgiveness, the grace of someone else taking you just as you are and finding in you an unsuspected goodness.[4]

Professional caregivers and trained volunteers serving in a variety of sectors keenly understand that assisting someone to feel less vulnerable, more accepted and ultimately more whole takes many forms. For instance, as people age, their suffering may not be connected as much to physical pain as it is to loneliness, or feeling like they are a burden to others. Emotional healing and wholeness can come when someone experiences deep presence, feeling less alone and more deeply loved and cared for.

Kim, a nurse with many years of experience caring for people who are aging and requiring support in a full-time care setting, speaks of her work with deep passion. Her desire is to be attentive to those who could benefit from some extra attention or even a hug. She is quick to explain, though, that often they have been the ones who have helped to shape who she is as a nurse, a daughter and a parent. She has told me on many occasions that after caring for the same folks for long periods of time, she often grows to love them and does her own grieving when they die. She tries to give them a little extra love and attention besides their pills, but feels she often receives more from them than she gives.

One story she recalls involves an elderly immigrant woman, Anna, who spoke little English. Her children visited often and were very attentive. For many years she had lived on a small local farm with her husband and their daughter who had a disability. They grew organic vegetables and fruit and lived a simple life. Kim cared for her in a long-term-care home in a small community. As Anna's condition changed and she was dying, Kim asked Anna's daughter if she would like her mother moved to a single palliative care room to give them more privacy. Her daughter chose not to move her, as her mother was very close to her roommate, and they didn't want to worry her roommate with the move.

Kim fondly recalls that "The night she died, I was doing my rounds and found her daughter lying with her mom in the small narrow bed. With mom on her side, the daughter had snuggled her body behind her and had her arms wrapped around her mama. She was gently singing to her and holding her. It was profoundly moving and beautiful for me to witness, and I still get teary thinking about those moments. I cannot imagine anything more comforting than to be held by your own child as you lay dying, and to know and feel that love and comfort. This is a gift I hope I am able to share with my own family as our lives go on."

Healing, like pain and suffering, takes many forms. In hospice palliative care, we often speak of a person's total pain when we try to assess their care needs. This encompasses not only their physical symptoms, which can be profound at the end of life, but also emotional or existential pain. This type of distress often intensifies when people move closer to death, as they and their loved ones deal with difficult emotions and ask life's big questions connected to meaning, dying and beliefs. Caring for people who are living with a life-threatening illness calls us to constantly look at all the factors that contribute to their suffering. Attention to the whole person, as well as their loved ones who are also suffering, can help lead to deeper healing and a feeling of wholeness despite the presence of physical deterioration and continued grief and sadness.

Reflecting on this type of suffering and healing reminds me of a young woman I will call Sylvia. Before Sylvia came to live at the hospice, she spent a lot of time living in a local motel, as her cancer was complicated by many years of substance abuse. The nurses caring for her in the community knew she would benefit from our ability to address her physical, emotional and psychological needs if she were to agree to live at hospice. It was a tough sell, but she eventually agreed to make the move.

It was nice for us to have time with her for a month or so before her death. We were able to get to know her and to help her with not only her physical symptoms but some of her inner struggles. She admitted to feeling judged all of her life about her lifestyle and her choices. Yet we welcomed her with open arms and pampered her with bubble baths and lotion. One of our staff, who Sylvia really connected with, brought her a new nightgown. You would have thought she had given Sylvia a million dollars! Sylvia spent a lot of time in tears that first week. It was hard to tell whether they were tears of joy or sadness – or both. Over and over she cried, "I don't deserve this kind of treatment. I don't deserve to be here." Her feelings of unworthiness began to melt as we cared for her and listened with nonjudgmental ears and hearts. She confided that she had rarely experienced love and compassion that did not require something in return.

This type of care was hard for her to receive at first, but as the weeks went on, she became less suspicious of our motives. We were thrilled to see her soften and blossom, becoming more open and more comfortable with us and with herself on many levels. This ability to open her heart allowed for some deep healing to take place between herself and her teenage son, from whom she was mostly estranged. His healing was also evident; he was able to have some closure with his mom before she died.

Sylvia also had a boyfriend who treated her well and loved her a lot. He was able to spend lots of time with her, and there was healing and growth in their relationship as well. He felt like we accepted him, too; after she died, he would drop by hospice now and then for coffee, or just to sit in the spiritual space or the courtyard, remembering their time there together. Healing comes in many forms, even in the midst of continued grief and pain. Many of us were touched by our own encounters with Sylvia and the mutuality that occurred as we tried to treat her as a woman who was worthy and deserving of the kind of care we were able to offer. She taught us much about dignity, acceptance and learning how to receive.

Questions for Reflection

1. Have you experienced mutuality in your caregiving? Recall a story or encounter where you were healed in some way through someone you cared for.

2. Are there times you have recognized healing that was not related to physical pain? Reflect on an instance of this and how it has shaped you in the way you care for others or the way you assess the needs of those you care for.

Wounded Healers

The idea of providing comprehensive, whole-person care can cause caregivers to feel inadequate. They fear they may not be able to fully address the many needs of their care recipients. Caregivers might find themselves wondering, "If I am allowed only a certain amount of time for the care encounter, how can I make a real difference in the broader aspects of someone's healing or wellness?"

This sense of inadequacy can deepen as the caregiver reflects on their own vulnerabilities and any personal experiences in need of healing. As caregivers, our own grief/loss history, physical and emotional pain and personal spiritual questions are all part of our being. We bring all of who we are to the care encounter, since we cannot separate our personal experiences from the self that we bring to work.

Henri reassures us and encourages us to recognize that our wounds and vulnerabilities can in many ways help us to become better caregivers and healers.

> Nobody escapes being wounded. We all are wounded people, whether physically, emotionally, mentally, or spiritually. The main question is not "How can we hide our wounds?" so we don't have to be embarrassed, but "How can we put our woundedness in the service of others?" When our wounds cease to be a source of shame, and become a source of healing, we have become wounded healers.[5]

Reflecting on the fact that we are all wounded and vulnerable can help us to see that we are not very different from the people we care for. Buddhist teacher Pema Chodron explains that "Compassion is not a relationship between the healer and the wounded. It's a relationship between equals. Only when we know our own darkness well can we be present with the darkness of others. Compassion becomes real when we recognize our shared humanity."[6]

One of Henri's early books was titled *Aging*. Through the years, he discussed and discovered more about this concept of shared vulnerability as he reflected on his own aging and how we accompany and care with the elderly. In a speech he gave in June 1975, he offered some insights into this notion of mutuality in care.

> Those we care for often confront us with their many unanswered and unanswerable questions which can raise deep apprehensions within us, since they challenge us to raise the same questions in our own lives. … Those who ask for care invite us to listen to our own pains, to know our own wounds, and to face our own brokenness. … The great mystery of care is that it always involves the healing liberation, redemption, and

conversion, not only of the one who is cared for but also of the one who cares. When both come together in common vulnerability, then both experience a new community, both open themselves to conversion, and both experience new life as grace. … care only becomes real in a mutuality in which those who care and those who are cared for are both aware of their wounds and open to the healing gifts from each other.[7]

The education we received for our various professions was no doubt clear that the therapeutic encounter is not the place for us to reveal our own struggles or work through our own issues. The focus must always remain on the person receiving our care. Becoming aware of our own wounds or struggles does not mean we should share them at the bedside, or in the care setting, with the care recipient. Rather, our professional responsibility is to explore our own inner landscape and always be aware of and work through our own losses, struggles and wounds so we do not impose them onto those we care for. Doing our own inner work and being healthy enough to care for others is an important gift we give to everyone in our personal and professional lives, and a gift we give ourselves. Henri explains how this relates to being a wounded healer.

To enter into solidarity with a suffering person does not mean that we have to talk with that person about our own suffering. Speaking about our own wounds is seldom helpful to someone who is in pain. A wounded healer is someone who can listen to a person in pain without having to speak about his or her own wounds. When we have lived through a painful depression, we can listen with great attentiveness and love to a depressed friend without mentioning our experience. Mostly it is better not to direct a suffering person's attention to ourselves. We have to trust that our own bandaged wounds will allow us to listen to others with our whole being. That is healing.[8]

Becoming more self-aware can help us to be open to the healing that others can gift us with as they share their wounds and we accompany them. In our book *Embracing the End of Life: Help for Those Who Accompany the Dying,* Eugene Dufour and I speak about this essence of mutuality. We refer to caring as a partnership. We propose that we call ourselves care part-ners rather than care givers, since we believe that true healing happens when both parties enter into the relationship equally: "Caring is a partnership where one person reveals their pain, brokenness and vulnerability to another, and through develop-ing a relationship of trust, they work together towards healing and wholeness."[9] This does not mean that the care provider reveals their brokenness and vulnerability to the care receiver overtly, but that it comes with them into the care encounter inherently as a part of who the carer is. When I went to visit my cousin Walt in Suite One, months after my father's death in the same room, we talked about my dad and reminisced about our childhoods and our parents. I did not tell Walt that I was uncomfortable being in that room, since my father had died in that bed. The healing I experienced as a result of our visits came over time; I did not recognize that this had occurred until long after Walt died. In fact, these insights came to me only after doing some self-reflection around my ongoing work at hospice and its impact on my grief.

Understanding that we bring our entire selves into a care encounter invites carers to remain aware of the vulnerabilities and strengths of both parties, and of the possibility of mutual healing taking place. Being wounded does not interfere with our capacity to heal – in fact, it may increase that capacity as we enter into our caring with a sense of humility at not being perfect or having it all together. This element of mutuality and healing is illustrated in a story told by Jane Powell, a woman who worked with Henri when he lived at L'Arche Daybreak.

> Almost all people wish to have another person whom they trust simply be present with them at a time of in-tense grief. When Henri died suddenly of a heart attack

it was difficult for all of us at Daybreak. He had helped many of us in the community when other members had died, so that we especially missed his comfort when he himself passed away. I had the privilege of sitting at his wake with Tracy, a woman who needs much support because she has profound cerebral palsy. We sat together in silence on some cushions on the floor near the coffin containing Henri's body, with Tracy leaning against me. We had no words to share that would comfort us because Tracy does not speak with words and because my words would not have made our grief any easier. But being there quietly with Tracy was very consoling for me. We needed to be together. It was one of those privileged moments when our common humanity is evident and differences fade away.[10]

Henri's book *The Wounded Healer* contains a Jewish Talmud story where the Messiah is sitting among the poor, binding his wounds one at a time, waiting for the moment when he will be needed. Although the book was written for those involved in ministry, Nouwen explains that we must bind our own wounds carefully in anticipation of the moment when they will be needed. We must constantly address our own wounds so we can be prepared to heal the wounds of others. This speaks to the need for all those involved in the caring professions to engage in activities that will foster their ongoing personal and professional growth. Doing our own inner work and growing in self-awareness can include elements such as self-reflective practice, reading, spiritual care, counselling, mentoring, supervision and peer support. Besides nourishing personal and professional growth, self-awareness and self-care can help the caregiver to develop the resilience they need to protect themselves from compassion fatigue and burnout.

Questions for Reflection

1. Reflect on the concept that you are a wounded healer. What wounds in particular do you seem to be more aware of in your care encounters?

2. Do you believe that you have experienced the healing of some of your own woundedness through your caring? In what ways?

3. Do any wounds you carry need more intense attention as you continue to care for others? How might you begin to address these to aid in your own personal and professional growth and health?

Giving and Receiving Care

Most caregivers find it challenging to be on the receiving end of care. However, the notion of mutuality in caring can help us accept that it is just as important to receive as it is to give. Many of us grew up with the adage that it is better to give than to receive. While that may be true in that it can help us to grow without becoming selfish or narcissistic, caregivers are often guilty of caring for others at the expense of caring for themselves. What is called for is a sense of balance. Everything in the universe operates through dynamic exchange; giving and receiving are different aspects of the flow of energy. Is giving better than receiving? That is akin to asking if it is better to inhale than exhale; if it is better to be awake or asleep; if it is better to talk than to listen. All of these actions call for balance. One is not more noble than the other.

The difficulty arises when we insist on being givers but refuse to accept that we also must learn to receive. We somehow believe that independence trumps interdependence and erroneously equate receiving assistance or care as weakness or an inability to stand on our own. It can also perpetuate a distorted sense of power in the care relationship, assuming that "I am strong and you are weak." In his book *Aging*, Henri explores this idea with respect to care and the elderly.

We will never be able to give what we cannot receive. Jesus did not multiply bread before he had received five loaves from the boy in the crowd which he wanted to help. Only when we are able to receive the elderly as our teachers will it be possible to offer the help they are looking for. As long as we continue to divide the world into the strong and the weak, the helpers and the helped, the givers and the receivers, the independent and the dependent, real care will not be possible, because then we keep broadening the dividing lines that caused the suffering of the elderly in the first place.[11]

Those who spend much of their time caring for others – formally or informally – are not usually open to receiving care themselves until they are faced with a crisis and don't have a choice. A sudden illness, accident or change in their life's situation can cause them to grudgingly accept help and care from others. They initially may see this as a weakness or a sign that they are not able to do it all independently. However, once they are in this position, they come to learn that accepting care from others is not only a gift, but a necessity, and can help them to maintain their physical and their mental health.

Recognizing the need to allow others to care for us and with us, so we do not become depleted, is a lesson every caregiver needs to learn *before* a crisis happens. Being open to receiving care from others can nourish our soul, fill our cup and help to build resilience against the ravages of caregiver burnout and compassion fatigue. It also goes a long way in helping us to become a better caregiver to others.

Questions for Reflection

1. When have you been on the receiving end of care? Did you consciously receive it and welcome it, or fight against it? How? Why?

2. Do you seek out care for yourself? In what ways? If not, is this something you will change?

3. How has receiving care affected who you are and your ability to give care?

The Gifts of Presence and Listening

Mutuality and healing can only be fostered in the environment of presence and deep listening. In our fast-paced world it is easy to feel frustrated that we don't have ample time in our various roles to truly listen to each person and their story. However, I believe that every care encounter can lead to a deeper feeling of being heard and truly cared for by the recipient, if there is a genuine desire on the carer's part to listen and be fully present for whatever period of time they have. This is done while the care is being delivered, and can be done using our attitude, demeanour, caring voice, non-verbal communication and eye contact, to name a few approaches.

Dr. Rachel Naomi Remen tells us that "the most basic and powerful way to connect with another person is to Listen. Just listen. Perhaps the most important thing we ever give each other is our attention .... A loving silence often has far more power to heal and to connect than the most well-intentioned words."[12] Henri Nouwen expands on this for us.

> To listen is very hard, because it asks of us so much interior stability that we no longer need to prove ourselves by speeches, arguments, statements, or declarations. True listeners no longer have an inner need to make their presence known. They are free to receive, to welcome, to accept.

> Listening is much more than allowing another to talk while waiting for a chance to respond. Listening is paying full attention to others and welcoming them into our very beings. The beauty of listening is that, those who are listened to start feeling accepted, start taking their words more seriously and discovering their own true selves.[13]

Active listening signals that you truly care to be part of their experience. This can be difficult, since most givers are doers and our caregiving roles usually focus on being task-oriented. There are certainly times when we need to use our skills to deliver care through tasks we do. But we also must become comfortable learning to just be with someone and not do for them. After all, the very essence of personhood is that we are human "be"ings – not human "do"ings!

Focusing solely on tasks, at the cost of not being truly present, is sometimes the result of not feeling confident enough in what you have to offer as a caregiver. It is much more difficult to sit with someone and not say anything, if that is what is called for. It's easier to be productive, to find something to do or say in our attempt to relieve another's suffering. However, this urgency to do something – anything – can get in the way of facilitating the care they may truly need in that moment. In a well-loved quote attributed to Maya Angelou, we are reminded that the healing or the outcome is often not due solely to what we have said or done: "I've learned that people will forget what you said, people will forget what you did, but people will never forget how you made them feel." I encourage you to let that wisdom resonate in your heart often, as you focus on how people will ultimately feel as a recipient of your care. This quote also reminds us that even when we are afraid that we won't know what to say or do in a situation, healing can still be experienced because we took the time to show up and be present.

The Healthcare Provider Compassion Model

The understanding of the role of presence and compassion in caring has been further examined by Dr. Shane Sinclair and his associates. Shane established the Compassion Research Lab at the University of Calgary in Alberta, Canada, and secured funding that allowed him to undertake some seminal research in this field.

One study focused on *Compassion training in healthcare: What are patients' perspectives on training healthcare providers?*

This qualitative study set out to investigate advanced cancer patients' perspectives on the importance, feasibility, teaching methods and issues associated with training health care providers in compassionate care. Three themes emerged: compassion aptitude, cultivating compassion, and training methods.

The conclusion pointed to the fact that compassion is fundamental to the delivery of quality health care. It was felt that the results of this study could be used to inform future inquiries focused on knowledge transfer in devising curricula and tools to train and educate current and future health care providers in compassionate care.[14] After all, if compassion was seen as an important aspect of providing care, how would you measure that? What exactly are the competencies when training health care providers? Could compassion be taught?

Sinclair's research was published, and it included the development of a Healthcare Provider Compassion Model. Although it has been understood that health care providers were primary, front-line conduits of compassionate care, it was important to advance from what was largely a theoretical body of knowledge on compassion to more clinically informed evidence. The study focused on research with 57 health care providers from urban and rural palliative care services to generate an empirically derived, clinically informed model. "What are the Healthcare Providers' Understandings and Experiences of Compassion? The Healthcare Compassion Model: A Grounded Theory Study of Healthcare Providers in Canada" was published in March 2018.[15]

In the study, compassion was conceptualized as "a virtuous and intentional response to know a person, to discern their needs and ameliorate their suffering through relational understanding and action." Five categories and 13 associated themes were identified, depicting the dimensions of compassion and their relationship to one another.

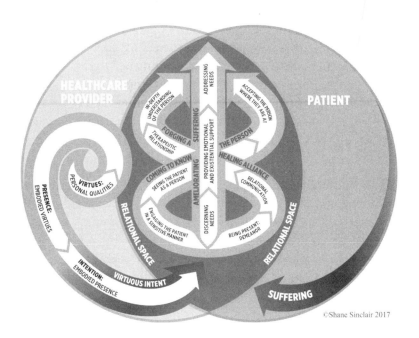

©Shane Sinclair 2017

Healthcare Provider Compassion Model

The large circle on the right depicts the patient entering the Relational Space from a state or a situation involving some aspect of suffering. The large circle on the left signifies the health care provider, whose initial response to the suffering person comes from the virtues, encapsulated in the category of Virtuous Intent. This intent includes

- Virtues – personal qualities
- Presence – embodied virtues
- Intention – embodied presence

In the Relational Space, where the circles intersect, the health care provider comes to know the person more deeply as they forge a healing alliance in the hopes of ameliorating their suffering. The health care provider does this by engaging them in a sensitive way, seeing the patient as a person and accepting them where they are.

This Healing Alliance is forged through
- Being Present: Demeanor

- Relational Communication
- Therapeutic Relationship
- In-depth Understanding of the Person

Ultimately, the Purpose/Hope/Outcome is to ameliorate the patient's suffering through discerning their needs, providing emotional and existential support, and addressing the needs that are identified.

It is relevant that many aspects of the model address elements of presence that the health care provider brings into the relational space, supporting the theoretical understandings of compassion that Henri and others have written about. "The first and most important aspect of all healing is an interested effort to know the patients fully, in all their joys and pains, pleasures and sorrows, ups and downs, highs and lows, which have given shape and form to their present situation."[16]

Ultimately, caregivers must become skilled at and comfortable with being fully present during their care encounters. In many cases, the encounter may not need to include words for healing to take place. The role of active presence and skillful listening should be a large part of all caring relationships, but even more so in particular professions such as psychotherapy, chaplaincy and social work, where their roles dictate using these to enable therapeutic conversations.

Active presence and becoming aware of the needs of the other are also fostered when there is an opportunity for ongoing care relationships, such as those in a residential setting or a long-term counselling situation. Bridget, a residential hospice chaplain who also has experience with the elderly in long-term-care settings, tells a story of Mildred, one of many care recipients who has taught her about the gift of presence. Mildred was a poet who now had a form of dementia. Although Mildred seemed to have lost the ability to remember her daily activities and her life stories, she had many memories and touch points to review over and over again in her poems. Bridget would often meet up with Mildred in her room. As Bridget came in, Mildred would exclaim, "Did you know that I'm a poet?" They spent much time together flipping through the pages of Mildred's anthology of poems, building a relationship based on being present to whatever evolved in the moment.

As time passed, Mildred's ability to follow instructions deteriorated because of her dementia. She had a particularly difficult time when she was awake for days and wandering endlessly. The staff, worried that she would fall, asked Bridget to spend some time with her. Bridget approached Mildred and gently asked, "Would you come back with me to your room?" This day, Mildred was not interested in poetry, but she often would sing during her visits with Bridget, so they began to sing. Bridget recalls this encounter with deep awe in what their time together was able to provide for Mildred. "We sat on the bed together, and sang and rocked. I held her, and slowly sang a selection of hymns and lullabies. Eventually, the rocking slowed and I prayed with her a familiar morning prayer. She finally lay down to sleep, and I was so grateful for the opportunity to be present to her that day. I know her familiarity with me was based on our ongoing relationship, and that trust played a large role in her allowing me to care for her in that way, even though she had long forgotten my name."

Healing can often come through the mere presence of someone who has taken time to sit at the bedside, or reach out to hold the hand or shoulder of another, without saying a word. I know I have encountered that experience both as a caregiver and as a recipient of care. Taking time to remember those moments and reflect on them helps us to be not only grateful for the encounter, but also more aware of the profound sense of healing that can take place at that moment.

Questions for Reflection

1. Have you ever just been present with someone in your caregiving and not done anything specific or task-oriented for them? What was that like?

2. Did you feel that it was caring enough, or inadequate? In what ways?

3. What has it been like for you to experience presence from another? With another?

Intimacy

It is truly a privilege to be invited into the lives of those we care for. This is something we must never take for granted. On many levels, we are invited into the very private corners of the lives of people who are particularly vulnerable when they allow themselves to be cared for by us. Since we often work in this milieu day in and day out, asking people to share their woundedness or reveal their personal care needs runs the risk of becoming routine actions for us. We must be diligent in remembering that this type of encounter is not routine for them. Having to be emotionally exposed to a counsellor, or undressed or touched in very personal places by a health care provider who is someone other than a partner or spouse, can be very difficult. It can easily bring feelings of shame, guilt and embarrassment to the surface. Taking steps to ensure that someone feels safe, protected and dignified as we care for them physically, emotionally, psychologically and spiritually is of the utmost importance.

A deep vulnerability and openness reveals itself in certain situations. This can be both profound and healing when caregivers are aware of the dignity and strength that intimacy in care can provide. I remember coming into the nurses' station at our hospice more than once and finding a personal support worker (PSW) in tears. When I asked her about it, she shared with me that she was overcome with emotion after experiencing a beautiful conversation with one of the women residents she had been bathing in a tub. There is something about being immersed in warm water, naked and exposed, that can move someone to express their deepest fears and vulnerabilities in the presence of a compassionate care provider who helps them to feel safe and dignified while offering their gift of presence and a listening ear. This PSW had held that woman's story in her heart, and at that moment knew she was very privileged for having taken part in that encounter. The conversation not only had a

profound effect on the PSW, it was also a breakthrough
resident in coming to terms with some of the struggles she hau
been having in living through her dying. A true mutuality in
care experience unfolded that day.

Although the intent of this resource is not to give specifics
about professional colleges and their standards, reviewing the
concept of professional intimacy in the therapeutic relationship may be helpful. The College of Nurses of Ontario, in its
Therapeutic Nurse–Client Relationship Practice Standard,
speaks about five key components of this relationship: trust,
respect, professional intimacy, empathy and power. Reviewing
these elements can inform our reflective practice as we ponder
their impact on our care encounters. I have slightly adapted the
language from the standards to fit care providers other than
nurses.

1. **Trust** – Trust is critical because the client is in a vulnerable position. At first, trust in a relationship is fragile,
   so it's especially important to keep promises made to a
   care recipient. If trust is breached, it becomes difficult to
   re-establish.

2. **Respect** – Respect is the recognition of the inherent dignity, worth and uniqueness of every individual, regard-
   less of socio-economic status, personal attributes and the
   nature of the health problem or care need.

3. **Professional intimacy** – Professional intimacy may relate
   to the physical activities, such as bathing, that care providers perform for, and with, the client that create closeness.
   Professional intimacy can also involve psychological, spiritual and social elements that are part of the care. Access
   to the client's personal information also contributes to
   professional intimacy.

4. **Empathy** – Empathy is the expression of understanding, validating and resonating with the meaning that the
   care experience holds for the client. Empathy includes

appropriate emotional distance from the client to ensure objectivity and an appropriate professional response.

5. **Power** – The professional caregiving relationship is one of unequal power. Although the provider may not immediately perceive it, they have more power than the client. The provider has more authority and influence, specialized knowledge, access to privileged information, and the ability to advocate for the client and the client's significant others. The appropriate use of power, in a caring manner, enables them to partner with the client to meet the client's needs. A misuse of power is considered abuse.

Earlier we discussed a sense of mutuality that can be present in the care relationship which can gift or transform either party. However, we need to remember that a power relationship is always present that must never be misused or abused. Due to the professional intimacy in these care relationships, maintaining therapeutic boundaries is essential.

Boundaries

Something that can keep the professional caregiver grounded is understanding and being attentive to the boundaries of the caring relationship. These boundaries refer to the many relationships that the caregiver will encounter, including the care receiver as well as their family and friends.

A boundary is crossed when the client's needs are no longer the focus of the care or of the therapeutic relationship. Such a violation typically involves a reversal of roles, secrecy, the creation of a double bind for the client, or the indulgence of personal privilege by the professional. Client consent to or initiation of a personal relationship is not a defense.

Boundaries can be blurred easily, so it is important for caregivers to reflect often on what is happening in their care relationships, especially if there is a sense that boundaries are being compromised. It can be difficult for care providers to be aware that they have crossed a boundary, since many violations

are unintended. As colleagues, we must be open with one another if we are concerned about what we are noticing, and help
one another to maintain healthy relationships. Giving colleagues
honest feedback and acting as a listening ear to those who are
questioning their situations is important.

As a care partner, it is difficult to avoid getting emotionally
involved with the people we care for. Active empathy allows us
to be a good companion to them. Remembering that we are
responsible *to* others, but not *for* others, can help us to avoid
taking the problems and struggles of our care recipients home
with us.

Finding a good balance in our caregiving roles is key. To be
warm, friendly and genuinely interested in the people you care
for can help with healing – while at the same time ensuring that
your friendliness does not cross into a friend relationship that
is inappropriate. Henri Nouwen also encourages us to reflect
on finding a balance.

> How many have left hospitals healed of their physical
> illness but hurt in their feelings by the treatment they
> received; how many return from their consultations with
> psychiatrists, social workers or counsellors, increasingly
> irritated by the noncommittal attitude and professional
> distance they encounter? ... the healer has to keep striv-
> ing for (developing a space) in which healer and patient
> can reach out to each other as fellow travelers sharing
> the same broken human condition.[17]

I have a colleague and friend, Michael, who works as a family therapist. This kind of therapy can lead to many complex
considerations of boundaries, as he often communicates with
different members of the same family about the challenges they
face. In one case, a couple came to him with their daughter,
looking for help in understanding how to cope with her anger
and aggression. They opened their hearts to him and shared
their own pain and confusion. During their work together, a
deep bond of trust and care developed.

When Michael finally met directly with their daughter, new limits and boundaries had to be set with the parents to protect the confidentiality of the healing work their daughter was pursuing. As much as they wanted to know what she was feeling and experiencing in her own therapy and help her with her struggles, he could not share what was going on with her or even accept information from them about what was evolving at home. At first, this was not easy for the parents to understand or accept, but they began to appreciate how important the boundaries were for their daughter to feel safe in her relationship with her new therapist. This process called for a delicate balance of intimacy, trust, care and respect for the needs of all concerned.

Questions for Reflection

1. Have you found yourself in a care situation where you struggled with a situation around intimacy or boundaries? How did you handle this? Would you do anything differently today to resolve it?

2. Have you ever had to set a boundary with another person that helped clarify the difference between being their caregiver and being their friend? What was it like for you? What was it like for the other person or persons involved?

3

The Challenges
of Caregiving

Caregiving can be lonely and hard.
It also changes us because we go into deep waters
and return to the surface with something
that can only come from the deep.

Despite the many gifts and benefits we receive from caring for others, there are definitely challenges with the role. This is true whether you are a family member or friend providing care, or are caring for others in a professional capacity. Some of the common challenges for the professional caregiver include but are not limited to what follows:

- **Physical** – physical strains; strain of travel; stress; not enough time/help; work-related injuries; sleep disturbances; working despite personal illness; effects of shift work; fatigue
- **Emotional** – grief on many levels; frustration; guilt; shame; isolation; feeling totally overwhelmed/unsupported; loneliness; hopelessness; anxiety
- **Mental** – difficulties with memory, brain function and communication; mental exhaustion; anxiety; endless tasks and lists of things to be done; mental stress; wishing you could do more; depression; vicarious trauma; compassion fatigue

- **Balancing tensions** – not enough time to do the work the way you would like to; addressing tensions between family members/clients; giving people as much freedom as possible to make their own choices (whether you agree or not); moral distress; values of the organization vs. your personal values; balancing care budgets and hours; experiencing tensions between management, colleagues, clients and others
- **Spiritual** – living with unanswered questions; being at peace with loss; keeping faith, hope and love alive; letting go of control; embracing hard realities; developing self-awareness/ego awareness

Addressing the Challenges

It can feel daunting to begin addressing these challenges. Henri Nouwen candidly acknowledges, "There is often a huge cost to the caregiver, and sometimes the care we give springs not from a well of love and altruism but from a bitter sea of resentful duty and obligation."[1] The desire to focus on transforming ourselves as we address our care challenges can go a long way in helping us come to work, most days, driven by hearts of service instead of resentment. Chapter 5 contains more detail around the elements of self-care, self-reflective practice and other ways to build resilience to stay healthy in your care practice. If you learn anything from this resource, I hope you come to realize that focusing on yourself is not selfish. It is essential that you have what you need to be able to care for others, staying as healthy as possible in body, mind and spirit so you can do your work well and be nourished in your life and career.

In many cases, addressing these challenges includes three elements:

- **Support** – ensuring adequate support for yourself personally; identifying and using supports that are in the workplace; being a catalyst to help colleagues and organizations build in supports
- **Knowledge** – becoming more aware of the challenges you face and some of the evidence-based ways to address them;

seeking knowledge for how to promote healthy workplaces; avoiding the stress of carrying burdens that are outside of your control

- **Perspective** – sometimes changing our lens on the situation leads to a more positive outcome, which can include personal and professional growth and/or healing

Physical Challenges

Addressing physical challenges usually begins with ensuring we value and dedicate time and energy to caring for ourselves physically. If we are not physically healthy ourselves, we will not have the stamina we need to care for others. This includes ensuring our immune systems are not stressed, and trying to be in the best shape possible to undertake the kind of work we do. To honestly ask ourselves if we are eating right, getting enough sleep and exercising regularly is a good beginning. If not, starting with these – even making small changes – can help us to have more energy and strength to focus on our work and be less prone to exhaustion and injury.

Chances are you can tell when your body is not in good working order. Listen to the signs your body is giving you that something is off balance and commit to not only caring more completely for yourself, but changing what you can in your work situation to promote your physical health and the health of your colleagues. This might include ergonomic changes, regular changes to your assignment or diligent use of mechanical lifts, transfer devices or extra personnel to keep you safe from physical strain or injury. Giving in to the notion that our work environments are too busy to work safely will only lead to bad outcomes for everyone. Prioritizing our day differently and/ or working smarter can help us put our own health and safety first. Using the energy and passion we have to brainstorm solutions with our colleagues to make positive changes is time well spent. This helps us to address the ongoing frustrations that can paralyze us into inaction and despair if left unchecked.

Many work environments require us to do more with less. It can be a delicate balancing act between feeling like we are providing good care and feeling frustrated that we don't have time to do more. Focusing on what we *can* do, without shouldering the burden of the system changes that are outside of our control, might allow us to work with more realistic expectations. This perspective can enable us to leave work at the end of the day reflecting on what we were able to accomplish and how we made our care recipients feel, instead of focusing on the things we were not able to get done.

Caregivers who work rotating shifts or drive for long stretches must be even more diligent in finding ways to maintain good physical health. Working sometimes 60 hours per week or more, between jobs, families and outside interests, can quickly leave us physically exhausted with few reserves. Added to that is the fact that we find ourselves at the mercy of digital technology, where we are in front of some kind of screen for most of our waking hours. We feel obligated to answer emails and work requests immediately, seven days a week. Given this environment, it is not surprising that sleep deprivation is now being called an epidemic. A pace like this can only be sustained for a short time before we begin to succumb to burnout and find our physical health in jeopardy.

Arming ourselves with knowledge, and looking at the latest research and evidence to make choices for healthy habits, is a good start. Reading articles and studies that support ways to maintain physical health in our field or setting and sharing those with leaders and colleagues can help both ourselves and our workplaces to consider even simple changes that make a difference. One of the best things we can do to address many of the challenges we will encounter is to set some boundaries between work, play, personal life and professional life, and not feel guilty or apologize for doing it. This is essential. I remember a friend who once decided he would not answer any emails on the weekend – work emails or otherwise. I wondered how he was going to manage this, but since he had announced it to folks, people did not expect any responses until Monday, so his plan worked. Setting and naming your boundaries takes some thought and perseverance, but it can be done.

My own story carries examples of physical care that was done well, and some that was not. For many years, although I was a busy mom and nurse, I did not do any regular exercise or stretching routines. As I have aged and been diagnosed with certain chronic diseases, I wished I had taken better care of myself. Still, I have become much more aware of how stress manifests itself in my body; I watch for signs of it so I know when I should be doing more focused work or making changes. For a long time, I struggled with sciatic pain, and was faithful to regular massage and chiropractor appointments to stay on top of it. In the midst of this, many factors came into play that led me to realize I needed a job change. The very day I left my old position, my sciatica disappeared! I had no idea how connected my pain was to my stress. I am now much more aware when something is not right and when I need to address not only my physical needs but the underlying causes.

Emotional Challenges

Self-reflection can assist us greatly in recognizing the emotional toll our role may be taking on us personally and professionally. Many caregivers work within environments of loss – working with people who become frail and/or die in their care. Others offer support in counselling or teaching environments, building relationships with those they accompany, then having to say goodbye along the way. Other losses we endure in our own personal lives, including losses of jobs, relationships, identities, pets and people, all add to the loss and grief we might be dealing with at any one time.

Loss is a normal part of our living. Being aware of how some of our physical and emotional struggles are attached to loss helps us to realize that these are usually normal reactions. Ensuring that we have a safe place to talk about our losses to colleagues or friends is a good start. The work of grief is telling the stories as we allow the loss to be transformed into energy that can help us to carry on. Henri Nouwen offers us some wisdom to reflect on with regards to examining loss.

When you are born, you leave your mother's womb, and you move to something new. When you go to school, you lose the family in a way and discover new life. When you grow old, you lose your job. Every time, the question is, can you choose to make these losses, these endless losses of your life as passages to something new? Can you choose to live your losses, not as ways to resentment, but as ways to freedom?[2]

Henri also reminds us that this grief can spiral quickly into resentment.

Resentment is a real option. Many choose it. When we are hit by one loss after another, it is very easy to become disillusioned, angry, bitter, and increasingly resentful. … Resentment is one of the most destructive forces in our lives. It is cold anger that has settled into the center of our being and hardened our hearts.[3]

Identifying when we may be feeling overwhelmed, not supported, lonely or hopeless in our work is an important step. Guilt, shame or isolation can be paralyzing. Finding a safe place to explore these feelings is important, before they pose a negative effect on our hearts and on the care we provide. If this is particularly troublesome for you, it may mean doing the soul-searching you need to make a job change or to seek professional help in examining how these feelings and your situation are affecting your life. There can be a compounding effect when these losses and our difficulties coping are coupled with the sense of resignation that many of our workplace realities are beyond our control. All of this adds to our emotional burden. Being able to work through these issues and realize we are not at fault for feeling this way is important. Some employers offer an Employee Assistance Plan where employees can access professional counselling. Doing this is a sign of health, not a sign of weakness.

Susan, who provides spiritual care in a community care setting, talks about helping others with their emotional challenges. She believes that a key part of her role is helping both caregivers and care receivers to speak honestly and name clearly what they find most challenging, painful or difficult. Being encouraged and supported to do so helps people to move towards recognizing and accepting their challenges.

> It is such a liberation for another who may be feeling ashamed and full of self-condemnation to be given unconditional acceptance. Pent-up fury only fuels resentment. and the support we can give allowing someone to release that goes a long way. When we help others acknowledge and accept the full spectrum of feelings they are likely to experience, they can actually begin to feel and trust their caregiving experiences as an enhancement and not a detriment to their lives. When people feel that they are held in a deeper way than they are used to, they feel safe enough to allow complex emotions to surface that may normally remain hidden.

Finding a safe place to be honest and open with what we are feeling is a great beginning to addressing the emotional challenges all caregivers face.

Mental Challenges

Maintaining good mental health is important both personally and professionally. Having difficulties with memory, brain function and communication can be related to physical exhaustion, stress, compassion fatigue, sleep deprivation or other work-related factors. Again, it is important to acknowledge that these are impacting your life and work, and try to address them. Being honest with colleagues and even leaders in your workplace can sometimes uncover similar symptoms in other people and enable you as a group to look at possible solutions. You must make your own health a priority, which may mean taking a leave of absence, changing assignments or even changing jobs to relieve any serious issues you are having.

Mental stresses at work can add to other underlying mental health issues that caregivers may be dealing with. Depression and anxiety are two of the most common ones. Paying close attention to your symptoms and triggers and reaching out for support is the key to maintaining mental wellness.

As caregivers, we need to be able to reflect on and name the hardest feelings and experiences in our caregiving stories. Unless we can acknowledge and express these realities, we cannot learn to integrate them or allow them to be reframed and healed. Formal and informal opportunities to do this on our own or with others can be helpful. These can include support circles, debriefing sessions, journalling and more. Although we have become better at addressing the stigma of mental health issues, we still have a long way to go. I have many colleagues and friends in caregiving roles who have been able to resume caregiving and maintain their mental health by acknowledging and addressing the effects of their depression or anxiety with combinations of counselling, leaves of absence, medication, support and establishing coping strategies. It is important for us to support, but also challenge, our colleagues to put themselves and their mental health first and not to be afraid to ask for help. Sometimes it is only when someone who cares points out what they are seeing that we will acknowledge our struggles and seek help.

In some instances, the solution may be to examine and try to rework your role. Amy Wrzesniewski coined the term "job-crafting" to refer to redesigning your responsibilities to better leverage your strengths. Take some time to reflect on what you enjoy and excel at. "The best part of my workday is when I _____." Consider focusing some of your energy on making connections with other colleagues or supervisors as well as with interesting people who are pursuing a path you admire. If you are dissatisfied in your job, or your job is making you ill, you are not alone. The good news is, you can often become more satisfied by making changes to your mindset and tweaking your role. If this proves futile, and you are still very unhappy in your role, you may have to consider changing jobs to maintain your mental health. This can be a scary prospect, but many people find it life-saving and gratifying, and often wonder why they did not do it a long time ago!

Balancing Tensions

Tension is a normal condition in our life and in our work. How much it affects us depends on how much is going on at any given time and our resources to address it. Again, good self-reflection is the place to start. Is the issue something that I can control? If not, is there a solution or compromise? Is the situation being clouded by any bias or judgment on my part that I can adjust? Is this a serious enough issue that I need to speak with others about it? Being able to discuss your concerns with someone else who can be objective and supportive is a good first step. If it is affecting your work or your personal life, you will need to find some balance or resolution that does not leave you feeling defeated or stressed.

Sometimes it just takes time for a situation to be resolved or a tension to be distributed. In our world of instant gratification, it is hard to wait for a natural evolving of the tension as time goes on or the situation changes. Learning to live with tension and at the same time to understand the element of patience is something Henri knew well.

> Patience is a hard discipline. It is not just waiting until something happens over which we have no control. … Patience is not a waiting passively until someone else does something. Patience asks us to live the moment to the fullest, to be completely present to the moment, to taste the here and now, to be where we are. When we are impatient we try to get away from where we are. We behave as if the real thing will happen tomorrow, later and somewhere else. Let's be patient and trust that the treasure we look for is hidden in the ground on which we stand.[4]

Staying with the tension – being honest and open about how it is affecting you and what options there may be, coupled with wisdom and patience – is often a good start in addressing it. Sometimes the source of the tension is a clash between our own beliefs about the care we want to provide and the vision or policies of the organization employing us. It may feel as though efficiency and budget concerns take precedence over what we believe is best for the people we care for. This can be difficult to resolve, especially in the current production-oriented climate we live in.

> In our free-market economy, they told me, human care is spoken of in terms of supply and demand. In this context, the suffering person becomes the buyer of care, and the care professional becomes the merchant of care. It seems to me that this language and the vision that underlies it reduce the human person to nothing but a commodity in the competitive world of high finance.[5]

Trying to maintain our beliefs about the care we wish to provide, realizing that we may be limited in what we can offer but doing everything we can to be totally present to that person for the time we are with them can help us to find some peace when we face this challenge. There are many factors we cannot control. Learning to work as well as possible given our circumstances can keep us from feeling totally frustrated and defeated.

Elyse is a young woman who has been involved in the field of social work for eight years. She has a rewarding, yet difficult role, counselling young people and families in crisis. She finds herself having to balance a number of tensions in her work, which include those inherent in the role and the organization and those evident within the clients and families she works with. It is easy to feel frustrated and disheartened dealing with mandatory caseload numbers, workload imbalance (too much to do with very little time), endless paperwork, ongoing system/agency changes, and the endless pursuit to gain more expertise to deal with the wide assortment of problems and issues that her clients bring to her.

Elyse has been serious about trying to take care of herself, physically and emotionally, since the beginning of her career. She believes that putting good self-care habits in place early will help her to stay healthy in this difficult caregiver setting. Although she confesses that it is easy to get caught up in the busyness of her life and let her self-care routines slide, she is aware of the need to keep nourishing herself so she has something left to give others. Her advice to other caregivers includes collaborating with colleagues and working as a team as much as possible, trying not to do it all on your own. She also tries to evaluate and re-examine her expectations and beliefs on an ongoing basis and sees a counsellor regularly to maintain her own mental and emotional health.

Spiritual Challenges

Although he was a deeply spiritual man, Henri wrote often of his own challenges in this area.

> The cover of *Time* magazine this week shows the face of Jesus, half of it holy, half of it sensual, and the cover story wonders whether the resurrection is a fable or a divine truth. All of this is very close to me. I realize that my faith and unbelief are never far from each other. Maybe it is exactly at the place where they touch each other that the growing edge of my life is.[6]

Reflecting on and nourishing our own spirituality, our own values and beliefs, and the essence of what lies in our heart and our soul is important – especially if we are charged with accompanying others who need to be able to express their own ideals and spiritual distress with us.

Our spirituality has to do with what gives us meaning and purpose in life. For many people, this can be tied to a set of religious beliefs or practices, but not always. Each person has a unique understanding of their world and their life, and it is not our right as carers to impose our beliefs on those we care for. We are called to care for each person in a non-judgmental way, supporting them and how they make sense of the world.

Our spiritual selves are usually accessed when we reflect on what our heart and our soul are asking, feeling or telling us. Our inner life puts us in touch with what is closest to who we truly are, outside of what the world tells us or our egos convince us of. The inner work of being able to regularly quiet our minds so we can see with the eyes of our hearts is spiritual work that can put us in touch with our Source of Life and Love, however we understand or name that. Meditation, reflection, spiritual reading, prayer and broadening our understanding of the lives and beliefs of others also help.

Situations in our work often intersect with our own spiritual life and beliefs. This can be a challenge. Identifying the tensions that arise in our hearts and minds, and trying to reflect on them and work through them, gives us the opportunity for growth and healing. Seeking out wisdom from others we trust who share our faith, our values, or our situations can be helpful. Trying to foster a life where we focus on creating a heart filled with peace can bring so much to those we care for. Etty Hillesum, a Jewish woman who was a prisoner during the Second World War, explains this concept in her own eloquent way:

Ultimately, we have just one moral duty:
    to reclaim large areas of peace in ourselves,
more and more peace and to reflect it towards others.
And the more peace there is in us,
    the more peace there will also be in our troubled world.[7]

Nouwen explains that the spiritual choices in our lives can often make the greatest difference.

Choices make the difference. Two people are in the same accident and severely wounded. They did not choose to be in the accident. It happened to them. But one of them chose to live the experience in bitterness, the other in gratitude. These choices radically influenced their lives and the lives of their families and friends. We have very little control over what happens in our lives, but we have a lot of control over how we integrate and remember what happens. It is precisely these spiritual choices that determine whether we live our lives with dignity.[8]

Henri also reminds us that the challenges we face don't have to define us. They can be opportunities for personal and professional growth and transformation. "But from the challenge of caregiving I truly believe it is possible to experience a more loving, mutual, and respectful relationship among us all – a spiritual bonding that carries new possibilities for mutual fulfillment and inner healing."[9]

Questions for Reflection

1. Name some of the challenges you have experienced in your caregiving. In what ways did you deal with them? What was most helpful? What might you do differently today?

2. What are some of the current challenges you face in your role as caregiver?

3. How do these challenges impact your personal life?

Challenges for the Care Recipient

"Many of us know from experience how hard it is to simply be a caregiver. At the same time, we may need to be reminded of how hard it is to be cared for. It isn't easy either way!"[10] Being the person on the receiving end of care has its hardships as well. As caregivers, how do we attend beyond the needs of physical or intellectual decline to the emotional and spiritual pain of those we care for? Henri speaks directly to some of these challenges:

Important for us as caregivers to remember here is that it is embarrassing to be exposed in weakness and to need help. Having managed their own lives so easily for so long for both themselves and others, those who are ill or weak may find it humiliating to have to receive care and ask someone else to help them, especially if the one asked is already busy and occupied with important matters.

Another very real sorrow for those receiving care is that it is not easy to wait—sometimes in pain—for someone to do for them what they can no longer do for themselves. It is bad enough for them to feel so fragile and so scared, but worse still to have to trust someone else—someone they may not know at all and who never knew them when they were strong. It can be humiliating to allow a stranger or even a family member to enter their intimate, physical, and private space. In other words, it is miserable for them to feel that they are the powerless one in the carer/cared-for relationship.[11]

As people who provide care for others, it is important for us to reflect on what it must be like for those we care for. This is the basis of our empathic and compassionate response. Ensuring that we always include them in our care conversations and allow them to remain in control of their care as much as possible is essential. I remember a friend telling me about a hospital stay where he felt invisible to the care providers. "I felt like a plant! I was getting the best medical care but the worst human care, and I felt ignored and objectified." Hearing this made me so sad and at the same time so angry. We all want the best for those we care for and care about. Reflecting on what my friend told me helped me to realize I must always acknowledge people who are there, even if I don't have time to engage them. I don't want anyone I care for to feel invisible. Our world today seems very focused on the rights of the individual. We seem to forget that this notion can be very isolating. Persons do not exist solely as individuals. They live in relationship. They are born into relationship, are healed and are cared for in relationship.

Another response we often hear from those receiving care is that they do not want to be a burden. Helping them to see that who they are as a person is more important than what assistance they require can help restore their sense of dignity and worth. Henri reminds us that the need for assistance as we age is part of the natural progression of our lives and our human condition. "The younger we are the more people we need so that we may

78

live; the older we become, the more people we again need to live. Life is lived from dependence to dependence."[12] We often forget that as children, we needed our parents and teachers and friends to care for us. We are led to believe that the ultimate goal in life is independence – a fallacy in a world that is truly interdependent, since our lives are always intertwined with the lives and decisions of others. As we age, our reliance on others is now seen as a failure to be independent, rather than a natural evolution of our human condition. "Our greatest suffering comes from losing touch with my/our belovedness and thinking of ourselves only as a useless, unwanted presence."[13] Helping people to understand that they are not a burden is key to helping them believe that they are valued, worthy and important. It is essential for us to remind those we care for that "You are not a burden for us – you are why we are here."

Often, people who refer to themselves as a burden are suffering from a sense of loss – not only of their sense of purpose, but also of their dignity. The term "dignity" refers to being worthy of honour, respect and esteem. Dr. Harvey Chochinov is a Canadian psychiatrist and world-renowned expert on the study of dignity and the development of a therapeutic intervention known as Dignity Therapy. His extensive research has shown that a caregiver's care tenor, or tone of care, has a profound influence on the person's sense of dignity.

> One of our earliest studies, published in *The Lancet*[14] reported that appearance, or *how patients experience themselves to be seen* by their health care providers, is the most ardent predictor of sense of dignity … Dignity affirming care tenor refers to the multitude of ways that health care providers convey appreciation, respect, and kindness to their patients. It may be a gentle touch, taking the time to sit at the bedside, or even the subtleties of body language that convey the message: *You are a whole person and deserve my time, my respect, and my care.*[15]

Chochinov explains further that "achieving a positive care tenor is usually not a matter of *more* time, but the *quality* of *time spent with the patient.*[16] This care tenor lies at the heart of "Attitude" in Chochinov's "A,B,C,D's of Dignity Conserving Care," published in the *British Medical Journal* in 2007. It falls in line with the Patient Dignity Question: "What do I need to know about you as a person to give you the best care possible?"[17]

Caring with an attitude and a care tenor that affirms the person's inherent dignity is profound. This reflection, taken from the viewpoint of the care receiver, may help us to remember their perspective so we can focus on providing care with dignity and compassion.

Advice from a Patient

This may be a normal day at work for you
But it's a big day in my life.

The look on your face and the tone of your voice
Can change my entire view of the world.

Remember, I'm not usually this needy or scared.

I am here because I trust you; help me stay confident.

I may look like I'm out of it,
But I can hear your conversations.

I'm not used to being naked around strangers.
Keep that in mind.

I'm impatient because I want to get the heck out of here.
Nothing personal.

I don't speak your language well.
You're going to do what to my what?

I may only be here for four days,
But I'll remember you the rest of my life.

Your patients need your patience.

Anonymous

Questions for Reflection

1. Try to imagine yourself as needing to be on the receiving end of care as a client served by your profession. What do you think would be most difficult for you?

2. Have you ever experienced feeling invisible? What did it feel like? Has it changed how you care for others?

3. Name some of the care receiver challenges you can identify from those you care for.

4. What else might your care receiver be experiencing that you tend not to see?

5. How can you make yourself more aware of what your care receivers are feeling or needing from you?

Healthy Caregiving

One of the most important pieces of advice that Henri gives us about caring is true whether you are providing care as a family member or caregiving professionally. "No, we shouldn't try to care by ourselves. Care is not an endurance test. We should, whenever possible, care together with others."[18] Surrounding ourselves with a community of care will not only help us to avoid exhaustion and burnout, but also ensure that we are mobilizing more help and allowing others the chance to care. Often we try to be a hero or feel we are the only one who can do the job right. When we engage others, including resources in the community or the family, the job becomes easier and even more satisfying for both the caregiver and the care recipient.

People who provide care for a living are at risk of developing fatigue, burnout or the more focused disorder of compassion fatigue. Charles Figley, a pioneer in identifying this condition, describes it as "a disorder that affects those who do their work well."[19]

The expectation that we can be immersed in suffering and loss daily and not be touched by it is as unrealistic as expecting to be able to walk through water without getting wet. This sort of denial is no small matter. The way we deal with loss shapes our capacity to be present to life more than anything else. The way we protect ourselves from loss may be the way in which we distance ourselves from life. We burn out not because we don't care but because we don't grieve. We burn out because we've allowed our hearts to become so filled with loss that we have no room left to care.[20]

The Compassion Fatigue Workbook, by Françoise Mathieu, is an excellent resource that explores in depth this "cost of caring" phenomenon and the issues associated with it. The workbook provides extensive information as well as creative tools for addressing and transforming compassion fatigue and vicarious trauma.

Compassion Fatigue (CF) refers to the profound emotional and physical exhaustion that helping professionals and caregivers can develop over the course of their careers as helpers. It is a gradual erosion of all the things that keep us connected to others in our caregiver role: our empathy, our hope, and of course our compassion – not only for others but also for ourselves. … Ironically, helpers who are burned out, worn down, fatigued and traumatized tend to work more and work harder. As a result, they go further and further down the path that can lead to serious physical and mental health difficulties, such as depression, anxiety, substance abuse, chronic pain, other stress-related illnesses, and even suicide. It is an occupational hazard, which means that almost every helper who cares about their patients/clients will eventually develop a certain amount of it, in varying degrees of severity.[21]

Some of the warning signs of compassion fatigue can include (but are not limited to)

- Becoming cynical, angry or defensive; not enjoying work; difficulty caring; absenteeism

- Physical signs: headaches, chronic pain, insomnia, i: immune system, exhaustion
- Feelings of anxiety, depression, numbness; feeling depleted, overly sensitive, detached, apathetic, emotionally exhausted, irritable; withdrawing from others; difficulty concentrating

Those who have a tendency to experience even mild forms of depression are at a greater risk of experiencing compassion fatigue. Other issues related to compassion fatigue can include these:

Vicarious trauma – experienced by care providers who become traumatized by images and stories they hear as they care for others, even though they did not experience the trauma directly. Vicarious trauma has been closely connected to compassion fatigue.

Moral distress – occurs when our job requires us to do something that we fundamentally disagree with. It can also happen when we are morally opposed to situations that may take place in our workplace. This type of distress can contribute to compassion fatigue.

Burnout – something that can also be experienced by many non-helping professions. It is identified as the physical and emotional exhaustion experienced when someone feels consistently powerless or overwhelmed at work. This does not necessarily mean that the person has lost the ability to feel compassion for others, as they might with compassion fatigue or vicarious trauma. Burnout can usually be resolved with a job change.

Disenfranchised grief – experienced when a loss cannot be openly acknowledged, socially sanctioned or publicly mourned. In short, while a person has experienced a loss, the person does not have a "right" to grieve that loss, since no one else recognizes it as a legitimate cause of grief. Dr. Kenneth J. Doka has done extensive work in this field.

So what can protect helpers and keep them healthy? Experts suggest building resilience. This can be done in a number of ways, and will be explored more deeply in chapter 5:

1. Ensuring attention to self-care

2. Improving self-awareness

3. Reducing chronic stress

Reflecting on the aspects of our work that provide pleasure and satisfaction can also be a helpful way to remain healthy. Experiencing compassion satisfaction can help us to guard against compassion fatigue; we can do this by reconnecting with the rewards of our work. You might consider reflecting on questions such as

- Why did I choose this profession?
- What keeps me here?
- How have I made a difference?
- Do I believe this is still the right job for me?

Here are some other strategies to support a healthy workplace and healthy caregivers:

Strategies for Staff

- Informal debriefing with colleagues through ongoing conversations – at staff meetings; at shift change; or at regular gatherings dedicated to this
- formal debriefing sessions, especially after a difficult situation
- watching out for each other; challenging each other to self-care; supporting each other; affirming each other; avoiding gossip and negative talk
- enjoying social time together; keeping in touch through smaller networks, support groups, telephone trees
- staying connected through social media (closed work groups); newsletters; gatherings
- finding ways of sharing memories; rituals; celebrating lives
- ongoing engagement and evaluation – providing feedback and suggestions to colleagues and management

Strategies for the Organization

- Naming and discussing issues, including compassion fatigue and mental health in the workplace; availability of a formal Employee Assistance Plan/support
- Providing a supportive work environment with regular opportunities for debriefing and decompressing
- Supporting professional development; peer support/mentoring; building leadership from within
- Adapting workloads when necessary
- Holding staff appreciation events; teambuilding exercises/ events
- Arranging for adequate resources; developing strong, compassionate teams
- Providing opportunities for supporting self-care – availability of complementary therapies; flexibility of work hours; attending to the physical setting being conducive to wellness
- Ongoing education, training, support; encouraging staff feedback and input
- Developing a "no blame" workplace culture and encouraging input, ideas, reporting of risks

In a 1996 interview for the University of Notre Dame, Henri Nouwen shared some of his own insights into remaining healthy in our caregiving and avoiding burnout:

* Burnout is giving without receiving. The caregiver always needs to review this perspective and support one another and see the gifts of the ones we care for.

* To be a good caregiver is to be really present – as in the ministry of presence.

* It is important not to be alone as a caregiver, and to be aware of limits.

* Caregivers have to realize when it's necessary for them to have a time out and not to feel guilty about it.

* It is important to be cared for yourself, as a caregiver. Who holds you? This is necessary so that you can be

totally there when you are caregiving, and trust that when you leave your presence will continue.

* One of the most difficult things is to be only half there – to be present but not want to be. This leads to resentment.[22]

My husband, Tom, worked in social services for over 25 years, supporting those with very little in the way of assets or income. He had a heart for his clients, treating each one of them with dignity and respect, often going above and beyond the protocols to provide them with what he could to make their lives a little easier. A variety of factors added stress to his job through the years, including limited budgets, added paperwork, new computer programs and clients who were dealing with more complex issues.

About a year and a half away from his retirement, I could see that Tom was becoming more and more withdrawn, showing signs of being anxious and probably drinking more alcohol than he would socially. He was losing weight as well as patience, and with his history of mild depression, I could see him slipping into that dark place again. With my new knowledge about compassion fatigue, I spoke to him about what I was seeing and what I was concerned about. After assuring me that I had nothing to worry about, and confessing that maybe he just needed a vacation, he agreed to visit our physician. Fortunately, our physician saw what I did and wrote him a note to be off work immediately.

After a few weeks of gentle persuasion, Tom agreed to see a counsellor. It was a good fit. He was diligent when it came to his appointments and doing the reflective exercises that were given to him. He also took up a new interest in reading, including some books to help with his inner work. At first Tom thought he only needed a few weeks off work; he was finally ready to go back after six months. By that time, he had renewed his commitment to eat better, go for walks and take breaks, continue with his reflective practice routines and make the changes he needed to give his self-care a higher priority. He returned to work healthy, and spent his final year in a good place emotionally and mentally, instead of feeling like he had to solely exist in his former state for one more year until retirement.

Lying Down in the Ever-Falling Snow is a compilation of studies and theories exploring Canadian health professionals' experience of compassion fatigue. The stories and statistics are sobering. Much more work and research must be done so that changes can happen.

> In a world of restricted time, limited resources, advancing job priorities, and fiscal agendas, compassion should not take a back seat. We believe that ethical, healthy, and safe environments can still flourish within constrained systems; relationships within the system can provide direction for this growth and sustainability. However, this phenomenon must be understood more completely if compassionate caring and ethical practice is to be sustained and compassion fatigue prevented.[23]

Questions for Reflection

1. What was new information for you in the section on Healthy Caregiving?

2. Have you experienced any of these conditions in your own caregiving practice? Explain.

3. What do you find most helpful about the suggestions for staying healthy? Which of these might you incorporate more fully into your own life? Can you commit to some form of regular self-reflection? What would that look like?

4. Have you recognized burnout or compassion fatigue in a co-worker? Have you extended support to them? Was that comfortable or awkward for you?

4

The Gifts
of Caregiving

*Because we who offer care and we who receive care
are both strong and vulnerable,
though in different ways, our coming together
in a caregiving relationship is an occasion to
open ourselves to receive an unexpected gift.*

Henri Nouwen

Growth and Transformation

Caring for others can provide opportunities for tremendous growth and transformation, both in the lives of the
ones receiving care and in the lives of care providers.
Some encounters will stand out and offer more gifts and growth
than others. The key to recognizing the gifts is taking time to
notice them, reflect on them and allow them to transform your
thinking, your understanding and your heart. So much of what
I have learned about courage, love, acceptance, patience and
more stems from encounters I have had with the people I have
cared for over the last 40 years of my professional life. Those
experiences and lessons, along with the learning and living

I have done outside of my work, have helped me to become who I am today.

For a number of years, I was someone who could react initially to some of our emergency room patients from a position of judgment. In our department, some patients would visit often for what seemed like no reason at all. We referred to them among the staff as "frequent flyers." Others had mental health and addiction issues; it was frustrating when they did not seem open to change, or were not compliant with the help being offered. As time went on, and I did more self-reflection, I began to recognize my own biases and how they affected my attitude and my care. This, along with learning, reading and watching mentors who taught me much about compassion, led me to work harder at finding out the true story of that person's suffering and withholding my judgment or remarks. Some of this I learned the hard way, after being gently corrected by colleagues who knew I was a better person than that. I also had a complaint made against me once by a patient's family; in retrospect, I had to admit I had not been the most compassionate person at two o'clock that morning, especially given the circumstances of their visit. It forced me to recognize my shortcomings, instead of making an excuse about how busy or how late it was. I came to understand that not only the compliments but also the complaints could be gifts to help me to grow and learn how to become a better person as well as a better nurse.

In *Courage for Caregivers,* we read the story of Judy, who was diagnosed with Parkinson's at a young age. She has had a lifetime of being cared for in different ways, but she can also acknowledge that she has likely given gifts to her caregivers: "I think I have given them courage," she mused, "maybe the will to put extra effort into something and not just do it carelessly. I've probably created patience in them because I have been such a pain in the neck sometimes!" And what were the gifts she had known as a recipient of care? "Definitely more tolerance of myself; more acceptance of my limitations; and willingness to ask for help. I've learned patience, and how to be gracious in receiving help."[1]

Spiritual writer Richard Rohr, a contemporary of Henri Nouwen's and someone I enjoy reading and learning from, has coined the phrase "Transformed people transform people." At our growing edges, we learn practices and lessons that can help us to transform our thinking and living. The lessons we learn from those we care for can be integrated into how we think and who we become. We, in turn, can often influence others we meet and work with as they grow and transform through their own journeys of living and caring. This ripple effect of caring is profound, and something worth reflecting on.

Questions for Reflection

1. What are some gifts and strengths you have discovered about yourself in the act of offering care?
2. Do you have any biases that you think may be impeding the quality of the care you offer? How might you try to address those?
3. How have your care receivers been your teachers?
4. Name a moment when you truly felt that your caregiving was a sacred privilege. How did that recognition affect you, personally and professionally?

Patience, Time and Gratitude

There are many understandings of the word "patience." Some might consider it an oppressive word, used by the powerful to keep the powerless under control. "Just be patient," we often heard our parents say, as we waited for dinner or to be given more independence. Others believe it denotes a passivity – a "waiting to see what happens." Webster's dictionary refers to it as "the capacity to accept or tolerate delay, problems, or suffering without becoming annoyed or anxious." Nouwen, who describes patience as something very active, offers us another perspective to consider. In one of his earlier books, titled *Compassion,* he gives us much food for thought, linking the discipline of patience to the virtue of compassion.

> (T)rue patience is the opposite of a passive waiting in which we let things happen and allow others to make the decisions. Patience means to enter actively into the thick of life and to fully bear the suffering within and around us. Patience is the capacity to see, hear, touch, taste, and smell as fully as possible the inner and outer events of our lives. It is to enter our lives with open eyes, ears, and hands so that we really know what is happening. Patience is an extremely difficult discipline precisely because it counteracts our unreflective impulse to flee or to fight.
>
> ... In short, patience is a willingness to be influenced even when this requires giving up control and entering into unknown territory.[2]

I would say that giving up control and entering into unknown territory is one of the most difficult things to do, yet it is an important lesson about the reality of the human condition and has the potential to be extremely transformative. We experience this so often as we care for others, and yet if we do not reflect on it, we can miss the richness of the lessons. People who live with a chronic disease or disability have had to let go of being in control and accept the limitations and the trajectory of their life and their disease. Health care providers, but also teachers and social workers, see this with both children and adults in their care. Those who are diagnosed with dementia have much to teach us about living the unknown. Being diagnosed with a life-limiting illness or moving into the final stages of life teaches us not only about letting go of being in control, but of recognizing the preciousness of time, learning to live in the present and understanding the concept of patience – even when our desire is to fight against it.

Henri Nouwen was convinced that our level of patience is deeply connected to how we experience the passage and usage of time in our everyday lives. With our lives becoming so entrenched in busyness, and our stress being connected to our seeming lack of hours in a day, Nouwen's reflections on the notion of time may be helpful. Perhaps some of the greatest gifts our clients can give us are related to accepting the lack of control they have over their conditions. These insights can go far in helping us to tame the lack of control we all truly have over the clock and the calendar.

What is the basis of this impatience? It is living in clock time. Clock time is that linear time by which our life is measured in abstract units appearing on clocks, watches, cell phones, computers and calendars. These measuring units tell us the month, the day, the hour, and the second in which we find ourselves, and decide for us how much longer we have to speak, listen, eat, sing, study, pray, sleep, play, or stay. Our lives are dominated by our clocks and watches. In particular, the tyranny of the one-hour slot is enormous. There are visiting hours, therapeutic hours, and even happy hours. Without being fully aware of it, our most intimate emotions are often influenced by the clock. The big wall clocks in hospitals and airports have caused much inner turmoil and many tears.

Clock time is outer time, time that has a hard, merciless objectivity to it. Clock time leads us to wonder how much longer we have to live and whether "real life" has not already passed us by. Clock time makes us disappointed with today and seems to suggest that maybe tomorrow, next week, or next year *it* will happen. Clock time keeps saying, "Hurry, hurry, time goes fast, maybe you will miss the real thing! But there is still a chance … Hurry to get married, find a job, visit a country, read a book, get a degree … Try to take it all in before you run out of time." Clock time always makes us depart. It breeds impatience and prevents any compassionate being together.[3]

My own aha moment while reflecting on this was connected to the phrase "Clock time always makes us depart." This "fight or flight" response, coupled with our task-oriented understandings of work, can lead us to miss the real opportunities to be fully engaged in the moment, the conversation, and the encounter with those we care for. Our struggle to be present, or patient, can keep us from experiencing a truly compassionate encounter. Our default seems to be to make excuses to ourselves and to those we serve, apologizing for having limited time to attend to their needs. No matter how hard we try to justify our speed or inattentiveness, it ultimately takes its toll not only on them, but on us – on our heart and soul. We subconsciously blame not only the systems we work in but ourselves, too, for the missed opportunities and frenzied encounters. More often than not, we become filled with frustration, guilt and resignation at the thought of being unable to bring about change.

Something we *can* do for ourselves is to let go of the guilt and look honestly at trying to be more mindful and more present, one encounter at a time. It is much less overwhelming to parcel out our workload adjustments in baby steps, looking at moments and opportunities where we can truly make a difference, than to try to conquer the entire beast at one time. I found in my own life that I was often the one who put those expectations of always being the perfect carer on myself. Once I saw how unworkable and impractical those ideals were, and offered as much compassion to myself as I tried to offer others, the challenges and situations became more manageable. It changed not only what I told myself, but also how I managed my time. This not only led to more fulfillment and satisfaction in how my care encounters went, but also assisted my perception of them and allowed me to celebrate the successes I had instead of only feeling frustrated. The gifts I received from my patients and those I ministered to in the parish were in the form of feedback and appreciation for being attentive to their needs, even when they could see that I was in the midst of a busy day. Their support kept me focused on being more intentional about my words, my attitude and my attention. Through them I slowly began to learn about the ways I could still do what I had to do, while being more present to them.

As long as we remain the victims of clock time, which forces us in the rigid patterns of time slots, we are doomed to be without compassion. When we live by the clock we have no time for each other: We are always on the way to our next appointment … If patience teaches us the natural rhythm of birth and death, growth and decay, light and darkness, and enables us to experience this new time with all our senses, then we discover limitless space for our fellow human beings.

… Patience opens our hearts to the elderly and prevents us from the clock-time judgement that their most important years have already passed. Patience opens us to the sick and dying and allows us to sense that one minute of really being together can remove the bitterness of a lifetime. … It is not difficult to recognize people who are patient. In their presence, something very deep happens to us. … In their presence, we feel how much we are loved, accepted, and cared for. The many things, both large and small, that filled us with anxiety suddenly seem to lose their power over us, and we recognize that all we really longed for is being realized in this one moment of compassion.[4]

Reflecting on our experiences of time can have redeeming qualities as well. The lessons about time being a gift is something that the people we care for teach us – especially those who have been told that their time here is limited. I remember when my father was told by the palliative care team that his condition was progressive and not curable. It was difficult for him and for my family to hear that. Through our tears, we turned the focus from his dying to his living. How did he want to live the rest of his life, whether it was two weeks, two months or more? Who did he want to see? What did he want to say to his friends and family? He led us all with courage down that path of the unknown. When an unexpected stroke fast-tracked his journey with end-stage prostate cancer, he became more debilitated and accepted that rehab would not change his overall situation. He made the decision to accept hospice care.

I had been involved in a wonderful project to help design and build a residential hospice in our city, which had opened only two months before Dad's stroke. On Father's Day that year, I was privileged to offer my father his final Father's Day gift: we were able to move him to a bed at the hospice I helped to build, providing a special space for him to live out the last few weeks of his life, fully engaged with his family and loved ones. The gifts he gave to each one of us there, including the staff, were tremendous. Besides his courage, deep faith and unconditional love, his keen sense of humour was a balm he caressed us all with each and every day. Once he accepted his prognosis and agreed to move to the hospice, he looked at me and proclaimed, "I'm ready to go to your place – the launchpad to heaven." From then on, we all affectionately referred to the hospice as "the launchpad," even including it in his obituary. He was tickled when a good friend dropped by to see him with a couple of bottles of wine to share, which he jokingly referred to as his jet fuel. His greatest gift to all of us was that he was not afraid to die, and he showed us all how to die with a heart filled with love, faith, joy and gratitude!

Many of those moments seemed to stand still for us as loved ones, and we continue to reflect on and gain strength from them. Poignant moments like these can be a reminder to us of the bigger picture of life, helping us to experience the notion of eternity, or timelessness. Touchstone experiences like this are important to return to: they can help to keep us grounded when it feels like things are spinning out of control. These profound encounters of timelessness can happen when we stand in awe before a beautiful lake, a sunset or a mountain vista. They can also occur during a care encounter when the tears being shared in our presence open the client's heart to healing, and open our heart to more compassion, empathy and joy. Henri's wisdom helps us to explore the essence of patience through this lens as well.

> [F]ortunately for most of us, there have been other moments in our lives too, moments with an essentially different quality ... moments in which we have a very different experience of time. It is the experience of the moment as full, rich, and pregnant. Such an experience makes us want to stay where we are and take it all in. Somehow we know that in this moment everything is contained: the beginning, the middle, and the end; the past, the present, and the future; the sorrow and the joy; the expectation and the realization; the searching and the finding. These patient moments can differ greatly from one another. They may occur while we are simply sitting at the bedside of a sick person and realize that being together is the most important thing. They may happen while we are working on a regular task and suddenly recognize that it is good simply to be alive and to work. ... We remember these and similar moments with great gratitude.[5]

Taking time to notice these moments, and to let them nourish us, is the essence of reflective practice. It is so easy to miss the beauty they can bring, even in the midst of pain, if we don't stop long enough to recognize and process them. One of the lessons we learned from my father, and something I have learned with many families I have cared for at end of life, is the gift of gratitude. Henri believed that this is the greatest gift we can offer our families and friends. "Gratitude as a discipline involves a conscious choice. I can choose to be grateful even when my emotions and feelings are still steeped in hurt and resentment. It is amazing how many occasions present themselves in which I can choose gratitude instead of a complaint."[6] Choosing to focus more on the gifts we receive than the struggles we experience can help us to build hearts and lives filled with gratitude, which can help to carry us during difficult times, both personally and professionally. Exposing our colleagues, friends and those we care for to our sense of gratitude can also promote more gracious encounters, which will in turn have a ripple effect on others. Remember, "transformed people transform people."

Questions for Reflection

1. What was some of your new learning on the concepts of patience and time in this section?
2. Recall a caregiving encounter where you learned something about patience. Describe what you learned and how it has impacted your care since then.
3. What does gratitude mean to you?

Joy and Sorrow

Although they appear to be polar opposites, Henri could often be heard referring to joy and sorrow as two sides of the same coin. He truly believed that even though you may be immersed in one, there was always a glimmer of the other to be held in the same moment.

> Joys are hidden in sorrows! I know this from my own times of depression. I know it from living with people [with disabilities]. I know it from looking into the eyes of patients, and from being with the poorest of the poor. We keep forgetting this truth and become overwhelmed by our own darkness. We easily lose sight of our joys and speak of our sorrows as the only reality there is.[7]

> Joy is hidden in compassion. The word compassion literally means "to suffer with." It seems quite unlikely that suffering with another person would bring joy. Yet being with a person in pain, offering simple presence to someone in despair, sharing with a friend times of confusion and uncertainty ... such experiences can bring us deep joy. Not happiness, not excitement, not great satisfaction, but the quiet joy of being there for someone

else and living in deep solidarity with our brothers and sisters in this human family. Often there is a solidarity in weakness, in woundedness, but it leads to the center of joy, which is sharing our humanity with others.[8]

When I think of those who have gifted me with joy, they are often people who have suffered under extreme circumstances, and yet have been able to find something to be thankful for and joyful about and to share that with me. They have taught me much about what is important in life, and that it is easy to miss the joy in the midst of the sorrow. People who have had family members dealing with conditions like ALS and end-stage cancers have given me glimpses of joy that shone through their obvious times of sorrow. This kind of joy is not to be confused with happiness, but rather the finding of a deep meaning and shining light while surrounded by darkness. Henri writes about his care relationship with Adam, giving us a great illustration of the kind of joy that compassion can bring.

> The joy that compassion brings is one of the best-kept secrets of humanity. It is a secret known to only a very few people, a secret that has to be rediscovered over and over again.
>
> I have had a few glimpses of it. When I came to Daybreak, a community with people who have mental disabilities, I was asked to spend a few hours with Adam, one of the handicapped members of the community. Each morning I had to get him out of bed, give him a bath, shave him, brush his teeth, comb his hair, dress him, walk him to the kitchen, give him his breakfast, and bring him to the place where he spends his day. During the first few weeks, I was mostly afraid, always worrying that I would do something wrong or that he would have an epileptic seizure. But gradually I relaxed and started to enjoy our daily routine. As the weeks passed by, I discovered how I had come to look forward to my two hours with Adam. Whenever I thought of him

during the day, I experienced gratitude for having him as my friend. Even though he couldn't speak or even give a sign of recognition, there was real love between us. My time with Adam had become the most precious time of the day. When a visiting friend asked me one day: "Couldn't you spend your time better than working with this handicapped man? Was it for this type of work that you got all your education?" I realized that I couldn't explain to him the joy that Adam brought me. He had to discover that for himself.[9]

The gift of joy that Adam offered to Henri was truly deep and heartfelt. It was a gift that would change Henri's life in many ways. Adam's needs and his vulnerability helped Henri to become aware of his own. Adam's openness to allowing Henri to care for him, and his responsiveness to Henri's ongoing conversations and care, contributed to this experience of mutuality and joy that Henri speaks of. Although Adam could not speak, we are made aware of his non-verbal responses in Henri's writing, which revealed that Henri's friendship in turn no doubt brought joy to Adam. It is during encounters like these that we can understand how shared vulnerability and weakness can lead to transformation and healing for everyone involved.

Weakness and Vulnerability

I love, therefore I am vulnerable.

Madeleine L'Engle[10]

One of the lessons that care recipients can gift us with is to not only recognize but accept our own weaknesses and vulnerabilities. Chapter 2 introduced us to the notion of being wounded healers and how our woundedness, instead of being a detriment to our care, can enhance the compassion and empathy that we bring to the care encounter. In other words, our own struggles and vulnerabilities can become our strengths. As I continue to wrestle with my own grief following the death of my father, there has been a new appreciation and understanding for the grief journeys of those I accompany. My heightened ability to connect on many levels to the story of the one facing loss has given me not only personal strength, but an added professional strength in lessening my fear as I reach out to provide care. This has made my caregiving more effective and allowed me to be present in a more profound way.

I find comfort in the words of Jean Vanier, who reminds us that

> To be human is to accept who we are, this mixture of strength and weakness. To be human is to accept and love others just as they are. To be human is to be bonded together, each with our weaknesses and strengths, because we need each other. Weakness, recognized, accepted, and offered, is at the heart of belonging, so it is at the heart of communion with another.[11]

Feeling vulnerable can provoke many emotions, including anxiety and fear. The people I have cared for, in particular those who are approaching the end of their lives, have often gifted me with the strength to overcome my fears so I can say or do what is needed in the moment. It seems as though whenever I am feeling inadequate or unsure, what I have learned about the ability to endure even in the face of death gives me courage to overcome the anxieties that arise during difficult conversations and situations. They have taught me that if I don't do or say something while I have the chance, I may miss the opportunity forever.

After Adam's death, Henri began to write about their relationship, and the effect Adam's friendship had on him. Ironically, Henri died suddenly seven months later. What follows captures some of Henri's thoughts as he views Adam's body and reflects on the profound gifts Adam shared.

> I couldn't stop gazing at his face. I thought, "Here is the man who more than anyone connected me with my inner self, my community, and my God. Here is the man I was asked to care for, but who took me into his life

and into his heart in such an incredibly deep way. Yes, I had cared for him during my first year at Daybreak and had come to love him so much, but he has been such an invaluable gift to me. Here is my counsellor, my teacher, and my guide, who could never say a word to me but taught me more than any book, professor, or spiritual director. Here is Adam, my friend, my beloved friend, the most vulnerable person I have ever known and at the same time the most powerful.[12]

Henri also wrote about Maurice, a man with Down's syndrome who lived at L'Arche Daybreak for many years. Those who knew Moe through the years spoke of the gifts of gentleness and joyfulness he so freely shared with everyone. In the days following Moe's death, Henri reflected about how Moe's life and legacy continued to shower gifts onto the community.

Of all the days that I have lived at Daybreak, those after Moe's death belong to the most intimate, the most uniting, and, in a strange way, the most sacred. A man who, through his fragility and weakness, had helped us create community during his life did so even more through his death. … we shared a deep sense that not only does life lead to death, but death leads to new life. The spirit of gentleness and kindness that surrounded and pervaded our conversation, the spirit of forgiveness and healing that touched each of us, and most of all the spirit of unity and communion that bound us together in a new way – that spirit was gratefully received as a gift of Moe who was dead and yet very much alive.[13]

Changing our perspective to see the strengths found in what we perceive as our weaknesses can help us to gain more confidence in what we have to offer those we care for. The culture we live in seems to measure the value of the human person by degrees of success, which can easily devalue people who are vulnerable, ill or disabled. Nouwen, however, talks about the power found in weakness, and how we must shift our thinking from needing to be successful to being fruitful.

> It's very interesting: fruits are always the result of vulner-ability.... "Alright, I am weaker and more vulnerable, but perhaps this can be a good thing. For instance, I depend more on people – people have to care for me because I am physically weak. Is that really so bad?" Well, it is bad if you think in terms of success but it might just be that others can be blessed and enriched in their lives by caring for me. In this way, my weakness becomes fruitful – I am still giving something. And by gratefully receiving someone else's care, I may be allowing them to discover something of their own gift, and of the beauty of love and service.[14]

The gift that I give to someone else by allowing them to pro-vide care to me was a new concept for me to grasp. It helped me to recognize the sacrifice of the gifts offered to me each time I care for someone. Even more, it led me to see that my role when others reach out to care for me is not to shut them down, but to allow them to provide nourishment and support to me so I can also learn how to receive their care and be refilled myself.

Indeed, weakness and vulnerability are profound teachers. Perhaps the greatest gifts they can give us are related to being able to trust as we learn how to let go of what we have no control over. Those we care for who face infirmity and death can teach us much about the true meaning of the words "power" and "powerlessness" and the roles they play as we continue living and caring with intention.

> Gradually, my body will lose its strength, my mind its flexibility; I will lose family and friends; I will become less relevant to society and be forgotten by most; I will have to depend increasingly on the help of others; and, in the end, I will have to let go of everything and be carried into the completely unknown. Am I willing to make that journey? Am I willing to let go of whatever

power I have left, to unclench my fists and trust in the grace hidden in complete powerlessness?[15]

Questions for Reflection

1. Describe an instance when, as Henri stated, you have experienced joy and sorrow as "two sides of the same coin."

2. Are there times when you have felt weak or vulnerable as a care provider? How did it make you feel? Did it have an impact on your care encounter? In what ways? Did it affect the person you were caring for? In what ways?

3. Reflecting on your care experiences, have you been able to find any strengths in what you may have perceived as your weaknesses? Describe.

Suffering and Solidarity

Another gift that our care recipients can give to us is a deeper understanding of the different ways people experience suffering, and how our responses can bring healing and wholeness even when we cannot do much to change their condition or their needs. Truly learning how to understand suffering, which is very subjective for each person, and how we can best respond – first with our presence and then, perhaps, with our expertise – is key. Reflecting on this deeply can help us to put our egos and our own needs aside, and truly focus on the needs of the one before us. Trying to assess, through our being present to them, where their suffering is radiating from and what their immediate needs are is vital. Many times we cannot alleviate all of their suffering, but the fact that they have a chance to speak to it and be heard can be very healing.

Frank Ostaseski, in his book *The Five Invitations: Discovering What Death Can Teach Us About Living Fully,* talks about how many times, caregiving and other helping careers don't look so much at what serves others, but what supports their own identity as a carer.

We want to be somebody who helps. We say, for example, "I work with the dying," with the emphasis on *I*. And so we invest in the role instead of the function. I call this "helper's disease" … the way we try to set ourselves apart from other people's suffering. We do this with our pity, our fear, our professional warmth, and even our charitable acts. It alters the way we make decisions.[16]

Frank goes on to tell a very poignant story to illustrate this for us.

Once there was a woman in our hospice who was just a few days from death. As she looked back on her life, she felt regret about many of her choices. As a result, she was quite sad – a little depressed, but not clinically. This seemed natural to me.

A visiting nurse pulled me aside after meeting with the patient and suggested that we start her on an antidepressant medication. This particular medication takes four to six weeks before its mood-altering benefits take effect.

"Why do you want to prescribe this medication?" I asked.

The nurse responded, "Well, she's so uncomfortable, and it's hard to see her this uncomfortable."

I said, tongue in cheek, "Maybe you should take the medication."[17]

Being with those who suffer is not comfortable. Many of the situations we find ourselves in as carers can evoke difficult emotions, including a sense of helplessness. However, upon reflection, we can begin to see these encounters and lessons as gifts that can hopefully teach us new ways to not only inquire and truly listen, but also to respond to the true needs of those we serve.

As caregivers, our default is often to assume we know what people need and move ahead with our tasks and our care plans without stopping to include the person receiving our care in an ongoing conversation. We like to believe that what we provide is patient-centred or client-centred care, but is it truly based on their needs, or our schedule and assumptions? Is it driven by what we are comfortable asking or providing? Does what we do in a care encounter truly provide the care receiver with a sense of being known or understood, or is it purely functional? Does it support their care or our ego? These are tough questions to grapple with, but are essential if we are to grow and transform ourselves as people and as carers.

Rachel Naomi Remen writes that "Helping, fixing, and serving represent three different ways of seeing life. When you help, you see life as weak. When you fix, you see life as broken. When you serve, you see life as whole. Fixing and helping may be the work of the ego, and service the work of the soul."[18] Frank Ostaseski adds, "Fixing and helping are draining. Over time, we may burn out. But service is renewing. When we serve, our work itself will renew us. In helping, we may find a sense of satisfaction, but in serving we find a sense of gratitude."[19]

Understanding suffering, wholeness and serving in this way helps us to see that we are all a part of the same human family. "Healing is not the outcome of an interaction between an expert and a problem; it requires a relationship between two whole human beings who bring to a situation of suffering the full power of their combined humanity and all of its potential. When this happens, many things that cannot be cured can still heal."[20] This gift of understanding our solidarity with others encourages us to be present and to care in new ways. It calls for a kind of caring that can be uncomfortable, but at the same time profound.

Love Is the Only True Medicine

Healers, therapists, friends, and lovers!

When you sit with a friend in pain,
when their world no longer makes sense;
when confusion rages and
no rest is to be found.

Just for a moment,
will you resist the temptation
to make things better,
to reassure them,
to provide answers,
even to heal them?

Will you offer your stillness, your listening,
your presence, and the warmth
of your immediacy?

Will you hold them in your heart,
with the same tenderness
of a mother holding her little one?

Will you embrace them where they are,
without needing them to change or transform
according to your own needs and schedule?

Will you stay close,
holding your own impatience
and discomfort near?
Will you look into their eyes
and see yourself?

Will you stay in the inferno of healing
with them, trusting in disintegration,
knowing that you are only witnessing
the falling away of an old dream?

Sometimes in doing nothing
everything is undone,
and love is revealed to be
the only true medicine.

Jeff Foster and Matt Licaa[21]

Questions for Reflection

1. What have you learned in this resource and through your caregiving experiences about suffering?

2. Are there times when you feel uncomfortable being with those who are suffering? In what ways?

3. How might you incorporate these experiences of suffering in your work?

4. What have you learned that can help you move forward in how you might approach those who are suffering, or who need your care?

5. How do you validate someone's suffering when you meet them?

6. Has being with people who suffer changed you? In what ways?

Courage and Love

We may define courage as being able to overcome danger, fear or difficulties. Henri Nouwen offers us a different definition:

> The word *courage* comes from the Latin word *cor*, which means "heart". A courageous act is an act coming from the heart. A courageous word is a word arising from the heart. The heart, however, is not just the place our emotions are located. The heart is the center of our being, the center of all thoughts, feelings, passions, and decisions.
>
> A courageous life, therefore, is a life lived from the center. It is a deeply rooted life, the opposite of a superficial life. "Have courage" therefore means "Let your center speak".[22]

I have learned about this kind of courage from so many people I have cared for – young people with devastating spinal cord injuries who find the courage to commit to lives of intensive therapy; those diagnosed with advanced cancers who undergo difficult treatments, including young children courageous enough to teach their parents and caregivers what perseverance is all about. I have cared for people who have been diagnosed with diseases such as ALS, and other neuro-degenerative conditions, who find the courage to be positive, often leaving a tremendous legacy of hope and love with their families and friends.

In my own times of reflection, I am so grateful to have been privileged to accompany these amazing people through their difficult journeys. I often wonder, if I were the one receiving this diagnosis, would I have the strength and courage to live as they did?

One of the people who has taught me much about courage and unconditional love has been a nursing colleague and friend named MaryBeth. At the age of 40, she entered into a second marriage with Wayne, a 47-year-old widower with three young boys. Their blended family now included five children from the ages of eight to 13. Two years into their marriage, Wayne had a devastating stroke, which left him with speech and mobility deficits. MaryBeth was able to take some time off work during his initial rehab therapy, but eventually had to return to her nursing job while continuing to care not only for him but for their children. Wayne's health continued to deteriorate over the years: he had a heart attack, then was diagnosed with prostate cancer at age 60.

I watched and marvelled at how she continued to cope and remain positive, despite so many setbacks. She explains in retrospect that "I loved him, and the thought of not being there for him never entered my mind. I felt capable of handling this burden." She was a strong advocate for him as he struggled with ongoing health issues, especially when some of their medical teams were not totally supportive of their choices. Her resolve, her strength and her love were key in helping him to live as well and as long as he did.

Wayne finally died at the young age of 64, after 17 years of marriage – 15 of those in frail health. Although many people felt MaryBeth should be experiencing more relief than grief when he died, she admits to suffering deep pain and loss, for which she eventually sought counselling. She will share more of her self-care journey with us in chapter 5.

I have also learned much about this kind of unconditional love from special friends and family members who have been in tremendously difficult caregiving situations. Watching their dedication in the face of despair, their continued care and presence for their loved ones when it was extremely draining and exhausting physically and emotionally, caused me to wonder if I could do the same, given a similar situation. Witnessing the changes in my mother-in-law who lived more than 12 years with dementia gave me many insights about this devastating disease and the people who live with it. After watching her own mother live and die this way, my sister-in-law faced the same destiny with her husband, Larry. Both she and our Aunt Gisele, who cared for years for Uncle Mark, taught me so much about unconditional love and commitment as they remained deeply devoted to loving and caring for their husbands until dementia ended their lives.

Caregivers reflecting on their caregiving experiences will often realize that they received much more than they gave. Taking time for reflection to recognize what we have learned and received from others is key. I believe that being able to use the lessons I have learned in my own life and my own caregiving is a profound gift. It has truly made me a better wife, friend, mother and, most of all, a better nurse. The gifts are always there, but if we do not stop to notice them, they will not help us to grow personally or professionally.

Sometimes we may wonder if it is all worth it – if loving and caring so much are worth the pain that often comes with suffering and loss. Henri Nouwen shares some wisdom for us to ponder:

> Every time we make the decision to love someone, we open ourselves to great suffering, because those we most love cause us not only great joy but also great pain. The greatest pain comes from leaving. When the child leaves

home, when the husband or wife leaves for a long period of time or for good, when the beloved friend departs to another country or dies, the pain of the leaving can tear us apart.

Still, if we want to avoid the suffering of leaving, we will never experience the joy of loving. And love is stronger than fear, life stronger than death, hope stronger than despair. We have to trust that the risk of loving is always worth taking.[23]

Questions for Reflection

1. Reflect on some of your own caregiving experiences and ponder the times you have learned something about suffering, courage or love. How have these experiences helped you in your life? How have they helped you in your caregiving?

2. Henri Nouwen not only published a large number of books and articles, he was also a prolific letter writer. He kept up an amazing volume of correspondence with hundreds of individuals over his lifetime. The art of letter writing is profound and can offer us both mental and emotional benefits. In your reflection time, consider writing a letter of appreciation to someone for the gifts you have received in caring for him or her. You may choose to share it or keep it to yourself.

5

Sustaining Caregiving

Care is not an endurance test.
We should, whenever possible, care together with others.

Henri Nouwen

Caring as a Community

Reflecting on our caregiving roles and the consequences for our well-being can be a daunting task. Often these roles become blurred as we find ourselves in a professional care role, sandwiched between our personal lives caring for children, aging parents, spouses, neighbours, friends or others. Providing care simultaneously in both our personal as well as our professional lives is commonplace, and its effects are cumulative. Fatigue and burnout don't have clear markers that identify the sources of the extensive caring we do, or indicate whether it is emanating from work or home.

How do we begin to maintain health and wellness in our own lives when we find ourselves burdened with providing care for others? One way to begin is to not be afraid to ask for help. Writer and researcher Brené Brown urges us to let go of the myth of self-sufficiency that is so prevalent in our society.

One of the greatest barriers to connection is the cultural importance we place on "going it alone." Somehow we've come to equate success with not needing anyone. Many of us are very reluctant to reach out for help when we need it ourselves. It's as if we've divided the world into "those who offer help" and "those who need help." The truth is that we are both.[1]

In chapter 4 we met MaryBeth, a community visiting nurse who was also looking after a husband who had had a stroke, as well as five pre-teens/teens. On top of those stressors, she was not in a work environment that was conducive to supporting her or her needs. She felt as though the management was devoid of compassion; although her doctors pleaded for her to be able to have assignments closer to home, this request continued to fall on deaf ears. She had friends and colleagues who made sure that she got out for lunch or dinner once a week, who tried to advocate with their employer on her behalf, but she was stuck in a difficult situation with no relief in sight.

Eventually, she was approached by another local employer who offered her a position on the palliative care team, which was her passion. Her new boss was more than accommodating and understanding of her complex situation, and made efforts to ensure her assignments supported her need to be available for her family. "It was the first time I felt valued as an employee, and supported in the huge tasks before me every time I drove into my driveway after work. Once I felt appreciated for my ability and expertise, work became a soothing balm for me." The support from her colleagues and friends continued as she took time to be at home, caring for her husband until his death.

Henri's wisdom in this area is profound. He makes a statement that should be shared with everyone who provides care for another – formal or informal. "No, we shouldn't try to care by ourselves. Care is not an endurance test. We should, whenever possible, care together with others."[2] As professional care providers, we must heed this message for ourselves, but it is also important for us to remind the family caregivers many of us work with that it is a healthy decision not only to ask for help, but to take it when it is offered. So many of them feel obligated or resigned to doing it all on their own.

People are generally afraid to ask others for help, yet upon doing so, find that others are more than happy to assist and were usually very glad to be asked. Often people reach out saying, "Let me know if you need anything," yet we fail to act on their offer. Putting our egos, our fears and our self-reliant attitudes aside is often all it takes to come up with a care and support plan that works for everyone.

Henri's reflections on the concept of community may seem somewhat counter-cultural in a society that values independence and individualism. Relying on one another is not only important – it helps to build stronger relationships and a connectedness that in many ways is lacking today. It is easy to live fairly solitary lives in our homes, keeping to ourselves for the most part. We tend to put up fences around our yards, and have given up the old habit of sitting out on the front porch and getting to know our neighbours. Many cities are now looking at adopting the concept of becoming "Compassionate Communities" that provide opportunities for people to look in on their neighbours and ensure there are resources to support those who are infirm or alone.

Reaching out to others for assistance can be a wonderful opportunity to build community. After all, we hear that it takes a village to raise a child; I believe that sentiment should be adjusted to remind us that it takes a village to live your entire life well.

> In my own community, with many men and women living with disabilities, the greatest source of suffering is not the disability itself, but the accompanying feelings of being useless, worthless, unappreciated and unloved. It is much easier to accept the inability to speak, walk or feed oneself than it is to accept the inability to be of special value to another person. We human beings can suffer immense deprivations with great steadfastness,

but when we sense that we no longer have anything to offer to anyone, we quickly lose our grip on our life. Instinctively we know that the joy of life comes from the ways in which we live together and that the pain of life comes from the many ways we fail to do that well.[3]

Another reality is that people often feel that they cannot ask for help. Sometimes they are blindsided by the weight of the burdens, and find it hard to think clearly. At other times, their fierce independence may prevent them from reaching out, convinced that others could never possibly do the tasks as well they do. Or, they feel they must be attentive day and night to the situation, and fear not being available or present when they are needed. That fear can be more about their own need to be needed than about the true needs of the person requiring care. Allowing others to help, and believing that it is not only a good idea but a healthy one to take a break from caregiving and step away at times, is another important lesson. Of course, all of this hinges on the availability of resources to help, which is a difficulty faced by many families who are open to assistance, but don't have enough available. Being creative and accessing volunteer groups in the community as well as professional support can be an answer.

Henri also encourages us to realize that even when we are not physically present to another, we are still offering support and care.

… community, like solitude, is primarily a quality of the heart. … community does not necessarily mean being physically together. We can live well in community while being physically alone. In such a situation, we can act freely, speak honestly, and suffer patiently, because of the intimate bond of love that unites us with others even when time and place separate us from them. The community of love stretches out not only beyond the boundaries of countries and continents, but also beyond the boundaries of decades and centuries. Not only the awareness of those who are far away but also the memory of those who lived long ago can lead us into a healing, sustaining, and guiding community.[4]

In my own personal reflection on this concept, I have come to realize that, although I may be off in another city working on a project, away from my spouse, or weeks or even months may pass between seeing my grown children in person, they are always with me, loving and supporting me. I know that in my heart. I do not need them to be physically present to believe that. Their presence continues even when they are not physically there. It is good for us to believe and understand as care providers that our presence, care and support continue even after we leave. Often the burden is great; we wish we could do more or had more time with each visit or appointment. Yet, the person receiving our care often understands and still feels very supported by even the little things we have done in short amounts of time.

> It is good to visit people who are sick, dying, shut in, disabled, or lonely. But it is also important not to feel guilty when our visits have to be cut short or can only happen occasionally. Often we are so apologetic about our limitations that our apologies prevent us from really being with the other when we are there. A short time fully present to a sick person is much better than a long time with many explanations of why we are too busy to come more often. If we are able to be fully present when we are with them, our absence too will bear many fruits. Our friends will say, "He visited me" or "She visited me" and discover in our absence the lasting grace of our presence.[5]

It is important for us to accept this reality in our own caring, but explaining this concept to family members who care for their loved ones is vital. It will help them realize they do not have to remain physically present day and night. Accepting help to have a break and get some time away will be refreshing; they often return to care for their loved one renewed in energy and spirit.

Universally speaking, serving others is important, and caring is a privilege we hold as members of the human family. Whether we provide care to others formally or informally, we are making a difference not only in their lives and our own, but in the community and even the world! There is a ripple effect to caring: one small gesture we make for another is often multiplied in how we respond the next time care is required, or how others respond because of our care and attentiveness to them. Reminding ourselves that we are not alone, and that the entire universe is reliant on relationships to survive, can help us to feel more comfortable not only asking for but accepting care for ourselves. This notion of our human connectedness as a universal community and our need for one another became even more apparent to Henri after watching a film titled *The Blue Planet*.

> As we look at that beautiful, majestic, blue planet as our home, we suddenly have a completely new understanding of the word *our*. *Our* means all people, from all the continents, of all colours, religions, races, and ages. Seen from the space shuttle, the many differences among people that cause hatred, violence, war, oppression, starvation, and mutual destruction seem ridiculous. From the distance of the space shuttle, it is crystal clear that we have the same home, that we belong together, that together we must care for our beautiful blue planet so that we will be able to live here, not just now, but for the long future. Our space age has made it possible for us to grow into a new consciousness of the basic unity of all people on earth and the common responsibility of all people to care for each other and, together, for our home.[6]

Questions for Reflection

1. What are some of the ways you have experienced the positive effects of caring as a community?
2. What are some of the difficulties you have encountered in trying to care or offer care in this way?
3. Name some of the strategies you might use to ensure that both the personal and professional caregivers in a care situation are receiving enough support.
4. Have you seen success with some of these strategies? If so, in what ways?
5. Have these strategies evolved through mutual conversation with the intended receivers?

Compassion for the Self

"Self-compassion is a practice in which we learn to be a good friend to ourselves when we need it most – to become an inner ally rather than an inner enemy. But typically we don't treat ourselves as well as we treat our friends."[7] Kristen Neff, one of the foremost researchers on self-compassion, has worked with another expert, Christopher Germer, on developing tools to address the part of our human nature where we can't seem to be as caring to ourselves as we are to others. Self-compassion is not being selfish, nor is it about having a pity party for ourselves. It is also not to be confused with self-esteem. Although both have strong links to psychological well-being, they diverge in significant ways.

* Self-esteem is a positive evaluation of self-worth. Self-compassion isn't a judgement or an evaluation at all. Instead, self-compassion is a way of *relating* to the ever-changing landscape of who we are with kindness and acceptance – especially when we fail or feel inadequate.

* Self-esteem requires feeling better than others. Self-compassion requires acknowledging that we are all imperfect.

＊ Self-esteem tends to be a fair-weathered friend, there for us when we succeed but deserting us precisely when we need it the most – when we fail or make a fool of ourselves. Self-compassion is always there for us, a reliable source of support even when our worldly stock has crashed. It still hurts when our pride is dashed, but we can be kind to ourselves *because* it hurts. "Wow, that was pretty humiliating. I'm so sorry. It's okay though; these things happen."

＊ Compared with self-esteem, self-compassion is less contingent on conditions like physical attractiveness or successful performance and provides a more stable sense of self-worth over time. It is also linked to less social comparison and narcissism than self-esteem is.[8]

It is natural for people to blame themselves when things don't go right, or to focus on their weaknesses and apologize for their shortcomings, even when things go well. "When we feel inadequate, our self-concept is threatened, so we attack the problem – ourselves! Feeling threatened puts stress on the mind and body, and chronic stress can cause anxiety and depression, which is why habitual self-criticism is so bad for emotional and physical well-being."[9]

Mindfulness is one of the foundations for cultivating self-compassion. We will explore that later in this chapter. When we look at the situation of caregivers developing self-compassion, another focus is finding ways to be compassionate to ourselves in the moment, especially if we are feeling stressed while we are providing care. Many of the self-care activities we tend to build into our lives happen outside of the actual care encounter, but it is important to be able to cultivate self-compassion in the moment. This is another way to protect yourself from fatigue and burnout and to build resilience. For example, if you are listening to a difficult story from someone you are providing care for, and begin to feel stressed or inadequate, take a deep breath and focus on not being self-critical. It is important to give yourself some compassion while experiencing the empathic pain of others. "[W]hen you calm and soothe your own mind, the person you're caring for will also feel calm and soothed through her own empathetic resonance. In other words, when we cultivate peace within, we help all those we're in contact with to become more peaceful as well."[10]

In *The Mindful Self-Compassion Workbook*, Chris Germer shares a story to illustrate how this exercise helped in a therapy situation he had with a new client named Franco. Franco confessed to Chris about the struggles he was facing in his life, including the fact that he had access to many medications, giving him comfort in the ability he held to end his life at any time. Upon hearing this, Chris immediately felt fear coursing through his body that Franco would try to harm himself.

> I realized I needed to try to stay connected with Franco despite my fear. I took a long inbreath for myself, reminding myself that this is part of the job of a psychologist, and slowly exhaled for Franco. Again and again I did this until I could listen to Franco's story with an open heart and less fear. I also reminded myself that I could not be responsible for saving Franco's life, but I would do whatever I could do in my capacity as a therapist. Breathing in this way, and reminding myself of the limits of my ability to control the situation, gave me space to feel Franco's despair in my own body. When I shared with Franco how moved I felt by his situation, Franco softened and began to explain to me all the courageous steps he was taking to stay alive and get through the crisis. When Franco left my office, we both had a ray of hope.[11]

Developing awareness and tools to practise self-compassion is essential, and the inability to do so can lead instead to self-destruction. Safe and effective use of self in caring for others is ongoing, since the primary tool in many situations is you. Assuming responsibility for your own inner work and developing the insights and tools to stay healthy in your caring helps you to provide compassion to yourself as readily as you do to others.

One key element to discover with regards to self-compassion is the concept of "enough." This includes not only that I know when to say "enough" so I do not overextend or damage myself, but also so I understand that who I am and what I have to offer at any given time is enough. I am enough by virtue of the person I am, in this moment. In his classic book *On Caring,* Milton Mayeroff talks about the process of life being enough.

The process of living is experienced as enough in itself when I live the meaning of my life. This does not imply perfection, however we may think of perfection. When we admit that a friend, a conversation, a musical performance, or a book is not perfect but is "good enough," it is not that we believe improvement impossible, but that improvement would not fundamentally change matters. Life is felt to be enough in the living, and what I want is simply the opportunity to live this life.[12]

One of my favourite authors, a former student and close friend of Nouwen's, is Wayne Muller. I have had the privilege to meet and work with Wayne, and he graciously opened this book with his foreword. His books *Sabbath* and *A Life of Being, Having and Doing Enough* have helped me to learn the importance of taking time, of self-care and of realizing that who I am in this moment in time is enough. Excerpts from the first chapter of his book on enough contain pearls of wisdom that can open up a new way of looking at our busy lives and inspire us to cultivate self-compassion and change.

We have forgotten what *enough* feels like. … We overload our expectations on ourselves and others, inflate our real and imaginary responsibilities, until our fierce and tender human hearts finally collapse under the relentless pressure of impossible demands. No living organism can sustain this kind of violent overwork before it breaks, or dies.[13]

I can remember vividly feeling this way a number of times in my life. I have always been one to say yes to many good and usually life-giving projects or roles that presented themselves. Notice I used the word "many," since they often existed all at the same time. However, time and again I would inevitably have to face the fact that I was juggling too much at once and that things needed to change. These moments were often thrust upon me at times that were not of my own choosing, and usually during a time of crisis. Physically and emotionally exhausted, and overwhelmed with fear and inadequacy, I would realize I had more on my plate than I could handle effectively, and was left with deciding what I needed to let go of to survive. An understanding and supportive spouse and family, rich friendships, helpful spiritual guides, and encouragement to take time for honest self-reflection helped me to learn to recognize when I needed to change what was happening. I had to learn how to accept and love who I was, despite my perceived limitations, and give myself permission to change course. These times were not easy, but were definitely moments of growth, both personally and professionally.

Wayne Muller's wisdom helped me to continue to show compassion to myself as my life went on. This reflection helped me put things into perspective.

> I meet so many doctors, nurses, teachers, clergy, parents, all of whom feel exhausted and overwhelmed, the weight of the world's sorrows on their shoulders, as if it is all, at the end of the day, up to us. It is not. We will not end hunger, poverty, suffering, or war at the end of the day, or the end of our lives. So then what *is* our job? Simply this: to be good, strong, and honorable stewards of the work during our lifetime.[14]

Questions for Reflection

1. Reflect on a care experience where you felt inadequate or guilty about what you could not offer the other. What was your mind's response? Your body's response?

2. What did you do at the time with your own feelings? Did you reflect on them afterwards? What would you do differently today if you found yourself in the same situation?

3. List some of the ways you currently try to offer yourself compassion.

Resilience and Self-Care

As people who care for others every day, our natural tendency is to be available to offer endless amounts of support – often at any cost. I see this especially if someone is that go-to person in the family or workplace who everyone looks to for the answers and who always steps up to the plate to take care of things. That is actually how things have shaped up in my life, so the lessons I have had to learn in self-care and the struggles I have endured when I have overextended myself have been tested in my own furnace of transformation. I have heard it said that sometimes you can get so busy trying to be everyone else's anchor that you don't realize you are drowning! Upon reflection, I can say this has been the case for me – more than once.

In chapter 3 we looked at burnout and compassion fatigue. These conditions, along with general fatigue, are often experienced by those who give much to others but do not take enough time for themselves – time to receive and be nourished, to fill their own cup. After all, you cannot pour from an empty cup. If you do not take time to fill yourself often, you will have nothing left to give – to your loved ones, yourself or your work.

Compassion fatigue experts tell us that to protect ourselves from fatigue and burnout, we must build resilience. The evidence in this area points to three ways we can do this.

Building Resilience:

1. Being faithful to self-care
2. Increasing self-awareness
3. Reducing chronic stress

Taking care of ourselves sounds like it should be easy. However, with our busy lives and schedules, it is easy to make excuses that we don't have time to take care of ourselves because we are so busy taking care of everyone and everything else! Self-care is not something to add to our already full to-do list or to relegate to an annual vacation. It must become an intentional way of living where our values, attitudes and actions are integrated into our day-to-day routines. To me, there is a moral imperative to making sure that we work diligently at this to remain healthy ourselves, but also to ensure that we have what we need to give to others. We deserve it – and so do they.

A good way to begin assessing your devotion to caring about yourself is to complete a self-care inventory. There are many different online resources for this, but one I generally like to use is listed in the resources section at the end of the book. People who complete a self-care inventory are usually surprised by two things – first, they are not as efficient at self-care as they might believe, and second, the range of activities and ways of being that are considered a part of self-care are very broad. In some circles, people might think that taking care of yourself simply means booking a massage or pedicure. Although these may be things you do for yourself, they are not enough. Some of the self-care practices I suggest are listed in the following chart:

Self-Care for Care Partners

- Take stock of what's on your plate/prioritize/ delegate/be selective
- Focus on ways to simplify your life/become more mindful
- Find time for yourself every day: quiet time; unplugged
- Identify what refreshes you and build it into your schedule
- Enjoy nature, the arts, music, hobbies
- Schedule time with family and friends
- Keep your sense of humour – don't take yourself too seriously!
- Maintain a personal life outside work
- Remember to play!
- Exercise, sleep and eat well
- Seek out support – personally and at work
- Take time to reflect on what you have given/ received
- Tend to your own spiritual needs/cultivate an inner life
- Learn the words "no" and "enough"
- Engage in regular self-reflective practice

The first task on the list, which is also suggested as Step One of developing a wellness plan in *The Compassion Fatigue Workbook*, is to take stock of what is already on your plate and in your calendar. It can be a sobering exercise to list all of your current responsibilities and determine how you spend your time. Factor in things like committee work, general home up-keep and projects, daily tasks for yourself and your family, work commitments, other care commitments, volunteering, studies, etc. For many people, this can be overwhelming. However, I have found it to be a useful exercise. It should not be a one-time event, but something you do once a year, when you are going through life changes or stresses, or are considering a new job. Take time during those moments to honestly list everything you are involved in. Our habit is to put more and more on our plates and never take anything off. Our lives quickly become overloaded and unmanageable, translating to little time for self-care and a fast track to fatigue.

I remember a point in my life when I was feeling stressed and overwhelmed. I had three part-time jobs (one with quite a commute) and a number of projects on the go, besides my busy family life as a wife and mother raising four children. I knew I was reaching a breaking point when I began having trouble with my health. I did some soul searching and decided to leave a job that I loved. It was a difficult decision, but I knew that staying would not be healthy for me or for the people I was working with. Taking stock of what was filling my days, being brutally honest about what I could handle and what I was being called to let go of, helped me to put some balance back into my life.

Sometimes you are able to delegate some of the pieces of your schedule to other people or family members, or prioritize which ones need the most attention and which ones can be given less, instead of removing them completely. In all cases, ensure that the pieces that nourish you and fill your cup remain a priority. In my case, one thing that always helped to nourish me was having lunch with good friends. Instead of casually saying, "We should do lunch sometime," I made it a point to set dates and put them in my calendar. Making these self-care elements a priority helped sustain my well-being. Finding time to meet with a spiritual guide each month and to make an annual retreat were self-care priorities, despite my busy schedule. Finding time every day to unplug from electronics or screens can be difficult, but it can help you learn to focus on yourself and what is truly going on inside your mind and your heart. This practice can also enhance your ability to provide that kind of attentiveness for those you love and care for.

Bridget, a hospice chaplain, is convinced that self-care is important, but knows that the reality of keeping it a priority is hard work. She tries to be faithful to yoga every morning, which helps her to centre herself and her spirit. She makes conscious choices to be unplugged as often as possible, even going so far as choosing not to have a cell phone, and keeping her personal computer use to a minimum. As an athlete who trains for cycling events, she prefers to watch little television, except for some professional cycling programs and the news. She confesses she would like to read more, but has little time or energy for it at the end of an emotional day.

Elyse, a young social worker who works with children and teens, has been serious about trying to take care of herself since the beginning of her career. Although she admits she is not always as attentive to these practices as she would like, her advice to others includes "Laugh often, learn what gives you energy, and ensure that you make time to do these things on a regular basis. Don't be afraid to confide in others; live in a mindset of gratitude; collaborate with your team and be aware of how your mind and heart are doing." Other advice is to "evaluate and re-examine your expectations and beliefs on an ongoing basis and remember most of all that it is okay to put your needs first. Taking your designated breaks and knowing that it is okay to say 'no' is not being selfish, but is necessary to continue to give of yourself."

Some of the items on her self-care list include

* Regular meditation and deep breathing
* Regular exercise and healthy eating
* Travelling and taking time away from work
* Having a "one day/appointment at a time" attitude
* Taking advantage of her benefits – e.g. massage therapy
* Spending time alone doing quiet activities such as reading
* Spending time with others, including family and friends
* Going out of her comfort zone and trying something new (learning a new language or a musical instrument)
* Getting plenty of sleep
* Enjoying simple pleasures such as a cup of tea or bubble bath
* Seeing a counsellor

When we learn about the importance of self-care and resilience, and what constitutes a healthy balance in our living, we become more able to see when others are having difficulty in caring for themselves and are showing signs of stress or fatigue. A good friend or colleague should consider speaking up if they notice someone who seems to be overextended, fatigued or burned out. Your first reaction to that may be "Really? Aren't we all just trying to get by? Isn't this the state of everyone who is caught up in their work systems?" Although there is truth to that, and there often appears to be little we can do to change our systems, we can still take the time to look out for one another. Speaking to a colleague you are concerned about is another form of caring. "I can't help but notice that you seem more stressed than usual. Is everything okay?" Or, just look at them with the eyes of compassion that you would use with your clients and ask them gently, "How are *you* doing?" Encouraging our colleagues to be honest with themselves and challenging them to good self-care is a gift we can give one another.

When my husband, Tom, returned to work after a six-month break to deal with stress and fatigue, his colleagues confessed to him that they had noticed before he left that he was not doing well, and apologized for not saying anything about it to him sooner. Going through that experience helped me to be more aware of how I support the people I work with; I am now passionate about encouraging others to keep an eye on the well-being of their co-workers. This is one more way that we all can provide care for the caregivers. We may not be able to change some of the systems we work in, but we can make the commitment to take care of one another along the way.

The systems we work in can certainly be a cause of stress. These include the many bureaucracies and organizations that support health care, social services, education, churches and other institutions providing care for others. Front-line caregiving becomes more burdensome with the added stresses of deadlines, paperwork, time constraints, quality indicators, metrics and other work pressures dictated by the structures and policies in place. The environment of doing more with less, and seeing the lives of those we serve affected by lean budgets and cutbacks, can take its toll on us. I believe that another way that we build resilience is to try to let go of the things we have little or no control over, and choose to concentrate on what we *can* control, which for the most part is the way we respond directly to the people in our care. Being mindful, positive and present can go a long way in helping to keep things in perspective. Henri shares some wisdom that may help.

> One of life's great questions centers not on what happens to us, but rather, how we will live in and through whatever happens. We cannot change most circumstances in our lives ... Very little of what I have lived, in fact, has to do with what I have decided – whom I have known, where I came into the world, what personality tendencies have taken hold.
>
> Our choice, then, often revolves around not what has happened or will happen to us, but how we will relate to life's turns and circumstances. Put another way: Will I relate to my life resentfully or gratefully?[15]

Questions for Reflection

1. Take some time to complete the self-care inventory listed in the resources section. Are you surprised by the results?

2. Introducing ways to take care of yourself and build resilience is not a one-time event, but must be ongoing. It is best to make a plan by choosing simple steps. Consider coming up with your own self-care plan and review it often:

   • What is one change I could make in the next WEEK?

   • What do I need to put into place to make that happen?

   • What is one change I could make in the next MONTH?

   • What do I need to put into place to make that happen?

   • What is one change I could make in the next YEAR?

   • What do I need to put into place to make that happen?

Self-Awareness and Self-Reflection

I have mentioned a number of times the need to engage in regular self-reflection to increase our own self-awareness and to recognize the experiences and gifts present in our caregiving that shape and transform us. Being aware of our beliefs and biases, and in touch with our feelings and emotions, enables us to grow, both personally and professionally. Mark Nepo, a poet and spiritual writer, eloquently inspires us to incorporate this practice into our daily routine: "Just opening quietly for moments everyday can create a path by which life can reach us, the way rain carves a little stream in the earth by which the smallest flowers are watered."[16]

Self-awareness has been described in many different ways, and is currently a buzzword in business management: it relates to emotional intelligence and the ability to be more confident and creative, build stronger relationships and communicate more effectively. Self-knowledge begins with taking the time to gain insights into how we compare our current behaviour to our internal standards and values. It is a way for us to become objective evaluators of ourselves.

Internal self-awareness refers to how conscious we are of our own values, passions, aspirations and reactions, and their impact on others. Getting to know ourselves can begin by reflecting on our family history, our cultural, racial and religious history, our grief/loss history, our relationships and our individual strengths and weaknesses. Remaining non-judgmental is an essential component of this work. Noticing what is happening inside of us, including our feelings, emotions and behaviours, must be viewed and accepted as an inevitable part of being human, rather than admonishing ourselves for what we find. Self-compassion is key when exploring our inner landscape.

Finding some quiet time by yourself, away from digital distractions, is a good way to reflect. Many people find that writing or keeping a journal is helpful. Writing is a way to reveal to yourself what is going on inside of you; it can help to sort out confusing and conflicting feelings and thoughts. Peer support, clinical supervision or counselling/psychotherapy can also support this introspective work.

External self-awareness refers to understanding how other people view us. Research has shown that people who recognize how others see them are more skilled at showing empathy and seeing others' perspectives. Seeking honest feedback from people we trust can help us with this type of awareness. Gaining self-awareness is a lifelong task, which helps us to grow as a person and can have a positive impact on our relationships as well as our goals.

Engaging in self-reflective practice is something that is not only encouraged, but in some cases mandated by licensing colleges for regulated professionals. Being able to look objectively at your learning needs and goals, your care relationships and performance, including feedback from colleagues and management, are some ways to ensure you are providing the best care possible and growing as a professional.

Self-reflective practice exercises don't have to be difficult or time-consuming. The important thing is that they help you to become more self-aware and develop into a regular part of your routine. Some suggestions might include the following:

* Begin the day by waking up a little early and sitting quietly with your coffee or tea. You might ask yourself some questions, such as these: How did my day go yesterday? How am I feeling generally? Do I feel anxious or worried? If so, what do I think might be the cause of that? What do I think I could do to relieve it? Are this feeling or any related behaviours in keeping with who I am or who I want to be in my role?

* Work in some solitude and reflection on a walk, on a country drive, while soaking in the tub or sitting on the front porch. Anytime you can catch some quiet and choose to leave the electronics alone and spend some quality time with yourself, you can build habits to both reflect and/or decompress and relax. Doing this often helps you to stay very close to what is going on inside, what is worrying you, what you are grateful for and how you are coping.

* At the end of the day, relax quietly and walk through your day. What was my best moment? What was my most difficult moment? How did I feel about my care encounter with Mr. Smith? Is there anything I would change the next time I see him? What did I do for me today? What will I plan to do for my own self-care tomorrow?

Raising self-awareness is taking time to be in touch with your heart and your soul, to see what is going well, what is causing you difficulty and what changes might help redirect you to live more in line with your own inner values and who you want to be.

Many people find it helpful to write down their thoughts or keep a journal. For me, journalling was a way to sort out my thoughts when my life and my mind seemed especially chaotic. I remember one time in particular when I was feeling overwhelmed: I knew I needed to figure out what was going on because my stomach was constantly upset. I sat down in the recliner with my morning coffee and my journal, took a deep breath, and started to write. I wrote about all the things that were going on and all the things that had happened in the previous weeks and months. Until I wrote them all down, I had no idea I had gone through so much. Being able to see it on paper helped me begin to sort through it and figure out what needed to be addressed first. It was cathartic to write, as I let go of some of the things that happened that I had no control over. At the same time, it was helpful for me to see *why* I had been feeling so overwhelmed. I could finally cut myself some slack for feeling the way I did: there had been a lot going on and I needed to step back and be gentle with myself. It made me feel less anxious afterwards, and I realized that I was coping better than I was giving myself credit for. It also changed my plans in moving forward.

In my earlier book, *Embracing the End of Life: Help for Those Who Accompany the Dying*, Eugene Dufour and I listed a number of helpful hints for those who might want to write or journal as a part of their self-reflective practice.

Prepare before writing – take some time to quiet yourself and relax; take some deep breaths and be sure you have set aside time without distractions in order to let your thoughts percolate and surface.

Find the right place – a comfortable chair or perhaps a spot under a tree, anywhere you may be able to be alone and inspired. Light a candle perhaps, or begin with a quiet prayer or meditation.

Consider the issue of privacy – do you want others to read what you have written? What will you do with these journals if anything happens to you, especially if there are personal issues which may affect the lives of others if your thoughts are revealed?

Gently begin to write

For a beginner, this may take the form of a letter to yourself or someone else, or perhaps to God. Others find writing in the form of poems or stories helpful.

Another way to begin is to just start naming how you are feeling that day, and what has been happening in your life. Often words and feelings start to come out which you hadn't realized were present. You can then look back at your journal entry and begin to see a picture of what is going on and perhaps why you are feeling the way you are.

Still another way to begin might be to pose a question, such as the ones we explore throughout this book. Give yourself time to think and reflect on your answers and feelings and write them down. You may be surprised at what actually comes to light.

Assess your well-being

How are you feeling about what is surfacing? Are you anxious, afraid, angry, confused, grateful or relieved? Identifying these emotions will give you a sense of what the issue which has surfaced is really doing to your body and mind. Our body, mind and spirit are all connected and one cannot control how these emotions reveal themselves, but being in touch with them can help us to deal with the real issues which may be surfacing in a physical manner as pain or insomnia.

Sometimes writing or journaling can put us in touch with difficult issues and feelings. These may have to be addressed more openly by talking to a close friend, family member or spiritual guide. In some cases, it may be best to speak to a doctor or counsellor, especially if there are deep and complicated areas to be dealt with such as enduring grief or painful memories that do not begin to ease even after they are identified and brought into the open.[17]

Self-care and self-reflection are not only important for our own health and growth, they will truly impact our thinking, our behaviours, our responses and our relationships, including the therapeutic relationships we are involved in when we care for others. Henri Nouwen experienced this in his own life and expressed it in his writings. "I definitely believe that we can only care to the degree that we are in touch with our own doubts and fears, just as we can only listen to the story of others with our own story in heart and mind."[18] Mark Nepo believes that the real and lasting practice for each of us is to remove what obstructs us so we can be who we are. "When we heal ourselves, we heal the world."[19] Learning to be comfortable with silence, to be in touch with our own feelings and stories and to become more mindful helps us to be more present to those we care for and to become a better listener. Self-awareness also helps us to understand our own "hot buttons" and those situations and experiences that might point to some unresolved issues that rise to the surface when we are with others, listening to their stories. Self-awareness will help us to recognize our scars versus our scabs. Our scars are there to remind us of the things we have healed from, although they have left a lasting impression.

Our scabs are signs of old wounds that keep getting opened up. Recognizing and tending to our scabs is an important part of continuing our own healing journey.

Questions for Reflection

1. Do you feel you have a high level of self-awareness? How would you describe your most important values, and how do you try to live them out?
2. What are some of the ways you already engage in self-reflection? What might you want to add to your routine? How can you make that happen?
3. Reflecting on your work, where and when do you feel most alive, most satisfied and most connected to your values? What about your work is life-giving? Life-depleting?
4. Have you come to recognize your own scars and scabs? Do you have work to do on healing your scabs? What will you do to move forward?

Developing Mindfulness

Jon Kabat-Zinn is a teacher, author, scientist and clinician who developed Mindfulness Based Stress Reduction (MBSR), in use in medical centres, hospitals and clinics around the world. Helping us to reduce our own chronic stress levels is part of the need to explore the concept of mindfulness. Remember that reducing chronic stress, along with attentiveness to self-care and raising self-awareness, helps us to build resilience. These practices not only keep us healthy as caregivers, but allow us to become open to caring and listening in a more comprehensive and deeper way. It can be a win-win for both the caregiver and care receiver.

> Mindfulness is awareness, cultivated by paying attention in a sustained and particular way: on purpose, in the present moment, and non-judgmentally. It is one of many forms of meditation, if you think of meditation as any

way in which we engage in (1) systematically regulating our attention and energy (2) thereby influencing and possibly transforming the quality of our experience (3) in the service of realizing the full range of our humanity and of (4) our relationships to others and the world.

Ultimately, I see mindfulness as a love affair – with life, with reality and imagination, with the beauty of your own being, with your heart and body and mind, and with the world. … the transformative potential of meditation in general and mindfulness in particular lies in engaging in ongoing practice.[20]

Mindfulness has also been described as an awareness of the present moment with acceptance. It is the opposite of multitasking! In *The Mindful Self-Compassion Workbook*, Neff and Germer explain that mindfulness is a simple skill because it just requires noticing what's happening while it's happening, using any or all of the five senses. For instance, take a moment to try focusing on what comes through the door of each of your senses, one by one.

* *Hearing* – Close your eyes and listen to the sounds in the environment. Let the sounds come to you. Notice what you hear, one sound after another, with an inner nod of recognition. There is no need to name what you hear.

* *Sight* – Open your eyes and allow your eyes to have a soft, wide-angle gaze. Again, note whatever you see, one visual impression after the other.

* *Touch* – Close your eyes again and notice the sensation of touch where your body meets the chair or your feet touch the floor.

* *Smell* – Put your hand up to your nose and notice any scents arising from your skin.

* *Taste* – Notice if there are any tastes in your mouth right now, perhaps lingering from the last thing you ate or drank.

While it is easy to be mindful for a moment or two, it is difficult to maintain that state of mind, because it goes against the brain's natural tendencies. Neuroscientists have identified an interconnected network of brain regions that is active when the mind is at rest and inactive when the mind is engaged in a task – *the default mode network*. Those parts become highly active when nothing in particular is capturing our attention, so the mind wanders.

This default mode network does three basic things: (1) it creates a sense of self, (2) it projects that self into the past or the future, and (3) it looks for problems. For instance, have you ever had the experience of sitting down to eat a meal, and before you knew it the entire plate of food was gone? Where was your mind? While your body was eating, your mind was elsewhere – lost in the default mode network. This brain uses its spare time to focus on potential problems that need solving. This is beneficial from an evolutionary point of view, so that we can anticipate threats to our survival, but it's a rather unpleasant way to live. Generally speaking, we are wired for survival, not happiness!

When we are operating in the default mode, we are often struggling, but we don't have the presence of mind to *know* that we are struggling. When we are mindful, we become aware of our internal narrative and don't get so lost in it.

Mindfulness gives us mental space. With mental space comes the freedom to choose how we might like to respond to a situation. Research shows that one of the benefits of practising mindfulness regularly is that it tends to deactivate the default mode network, both while meditating and during our normal activities. This means that the more we practise being mindful, the more opportunities we have to make better choices for ourselves, including the choice to practise self-compassion.[21]

Actively practising mindfulness, and being aware of when a situation warrants a deep breath and a change of focus, is helpful not only for ourselves but for how we care for and are present with others. Mindfulness is not about what one *does*, but how one *is*. In our busy work life, where we do not have as much time as we wish, it is crucial to be focused on how we spend that time with our patients or clients. Rather than being preoccupied with workplace distractions or things that are naturally on our mind, providing mindful care helps us to give the person in front of us our undivided attention. Working mindfully is actually more patient-focused and efficient, and can lead to fewer errors.

Frank Ostaseski gives us another perspective of how mindfulness can have a profound effect on our practice, for ourselves as well as our clients:

> I speak of my mindfulness practice as "a practice of intimacy." We can't know ourselves, each other, or death from a distance. This work is up close and personal. Meditation is all about learning to be intimate with ourselves, with others, and with all aspects of this worldly life, bringing the healing power of loving awareness forward so that we can meet what is scary, sad, and raw.[22]

Many mindful practitioners I know have developed a ritual before entering a counselling room, patient room or care encounter. They will find a moment to take a deep breath, to centre themselves and become aware of who they are and how they need to be present to the person or situation in front of them. The ability to draw on the best of who we are as care partners and to focus solely on the person in front of us, rather than on our own preconceived assumptions or agendas, can lead to a care experience that can be more healing and whole for everyone involved – including us. As Mark Nepo reminds us, "To listen is to continually give up all expectation and to give our attention, completely and freshly, to what is before us, not really knowing what we will hear or what that will mean. In the practice of our days, to listen is to lean in, softly, with a willingness to be changed by what we hear."[23]

Other aspects of becoming more mindful and developing disciplines that promote mindfulness include being more comfortable with solitude, silence and rest. In our busy, noisy, task-oriented world, these essential elements can seem counter-cultural at times. Yet, they are crucial in helping us to stay healthy ourselves and to become more proficient and mindful in our caring for others. Henri's wisdom helps us to see how these intentional times of solitude and self-reflection can be transformational. "It is in this solitude that we discover that being is more important than having, and that we are worth more than the result of our efforts. In solitude we discover that our life is not a possession to be defended, but a gift to be shared. … In solitude we become aware that our worth is not the same as our usefulness."[24]

In his book *Sabbath*, Wayne Muller reflects on the notions of busyness and rest.

In the relentless busyness of modern life, we have lost the rhythm between work and rest. All life requires a rhythm of rest. … There is a tidal rhythm, a deep, eternal conversation between the land and the great sea. In our bodies, the heart perceptibly rests after each life-giving beat; the lungs rest between the exhale and the inhale.

We have lost this essential rhythm. Our culture invariably supposes that action and accomplishment are better than rest, that doing something – anything – is better than doing nothing. Because of our desire to succeed, to meet these ever-growing expectations, we do not rest. Because we do not rest, we lose our way. We miss the compass points that would show us where to go, we bypass the nourishment that would give us succor. We miss the quiet that would give us wisdom.

… Our lack of rest and reflection is not just a personal affliction. It colours the way we build and sustain community, it dictates the way we respond to suffering, and it shapes the ways in which we seek peace and healing in the world.[25]

Becoming more mindful and intentional is not rocket science, nor is it difficult to begin. There are many good resources out there to help you learn more about mindfulness and mindful practices, including some we have named in the resources section of this book. I encourage you to find ways and resources that fit your lifestyle and personality which can help you become more comfortable exploring your inner landscape and being in touch with whatever moves your heart and your soul. The wisdom we all need to be exceptional caregivers is within us, if we take the time to mine it and bring it to the surface.

Questions for Reflection

1. Is developing mindfulness a new concept for you? If so, what can you do to begin learning and incorporating more mindfulness into your ordinary life and routine?

2. If mindfulness is not new to you, are you aware of how you are incorporating it into your life? Do you find it helpful? In what ways? How has it affected your care relationships?

Sustaining the Spirit

Sanctuary is wherever I find a safe space to regain my bearings, reclaim my soul, heal my wounds, and return to the world as a wounded healer.

It's not merely about finding shelter from the storm – it's about spiritual survival and the capacity to carry on.[26]

Parker Palmer

We have spoken about the kind of care we offer to others, and noted that it should support the needs of their body, mind and spirit. In the same way, the care we seek for ourselves must also be wholistic. How, then, does a caregiver care for their very heart and soul? How do we nourish and sustain our spirits? And what does that really mean?

The English word "spirit" comes from the Latin word *spiritus* – meaning "breath." The word "soul" is derived from the Greek word that refers to "vital breath." Speaking about the soul of a person refers to their *vital breath* – that which makes them unique. A part of nourishing your soul includes doing your own soul-searching to see what makes you *you*! Who are you? Where do you come from – your culture, your family, your experiences? What are your beliefs? What is important to you?

One understanding of the word "spirituality" refers to how we seek connections through our belief systems and relationships to something beyond or greater than ourselves – that which gives us meaning and purpose in life. For many people, this would include their beliefs and experiences formed within a religious tradition. Their faith and their understanding of the world in relation to something greater, their understanding of God, is often a foundation for what gives them meaning and purpose. However, those who do not aspire to a faith tradition are still spiritual – as all humans are. Our understanding of how we are connected to the world, and what gives each of us meaning and purpose, is personal and unique. Even those who come from the same family or the same faith tradition can hold very different ideas or understandings of this, and have distinct needs for what nourishes their heart and soul.

Your personal spiritual care, just like your self-care, is an inside job. You are the only one who knows what will sustain your spirit; it is important to make the effort to nourish your own heart and soul so you can maintain spiritual well-being, for your own sake and for those you care for and care about.

Parker Palmer uses the word "sanctuary" to describe the concept of nourishing his soul. "Sanctuary is as vital as breathing to me. Sometimes I find it in churches, monasteries, and other sites formally designated 'sacred.' But more often I find it in places sacred to my soul: in the natural world, in the company of a faithful friend, in solitary or shared silence, in the ambience of a good poem or good music."[27]

Bridget, a hospice chaplain, talks about how her reflections on the grace-filled moments she experiences help her to nourish her soul for her next care encounter.

I call them firefly moments. They are those fleeting moments that contain beauty and awe, sacred moments that seem to stand out from the ordinary. Like fireflies, you see them in your periphery, but may not see them again. For me, it's like a divine whisper, reminding me to "Pay attention – this is a moment of importance!" Moments like these give me strength to move on to the next room filled with pain and grief, and find something special to feed the soul – theirs and mine.

A smile, a touch, some sense of recognition from a loved one who has been unable to communicate – these special moments in a day of caring can inspire us to keep going when we feel like suffering overtakes our day. One place Bridget finds sanctuary is in being able to share her "firefly moments" with those who share the care circle she is in. For all of us, sharing stories about our care experiences can help us not only to process them, but to let them nourish or teach us. Of course, confidentiality always plays a part in what we say and who we can talk to. Still, it is important to find safe times and places to share these moments and stories.

Part of Bridget's spiritual self-care practice is to begin her day with yoga, which helps her to focus on both her body and her soul, to make her more mindful as she enters the day. She also has developed a gratitude practice, where she recalls moments that brought hope and healing to those she accompanied, and to her own heart. As Henri Nouwen would say, "Gratitude is the awareness that life in all its manifestations is a gift for which we want to give thanks. [Sometimes] what seemed a hindrance proves to be a gift. Thus gratitude becomes a quality of our hearts that allows us to live joyfully and peacefully even though our struggles continue."[28]

One way I feed my own soul and grow in spirit is through inspirational reading. Starting the day with some inspiring thoughts, articles or daily email reflections that interest me helps to feed my heart and keep my perspective focused in the direction my true self calls for. Quiet time with coffee and my journal has also helped my spirit grow. However, probably some of the most transformative times for me have been when I have taken time away to be on retreat.

There are many different ways to "retreat" or to step back, out of our ordinary routine, and set aside time to just be. Besides our daily reflective practice, and our efforts to be more mindful, it helps to take some extended periods of time in which to really reflect more deeply and become more in touch and aware of what is happening inside of us. This may be anything from a few hours at the lakeside to a few days of formal, intentional reflection. I have been able to take time most years to book an extended silent retreat at a spiritual centre, where I have places to walk, quiet time to write and meditate or pray, and moments to connect with a spiritual director or guide. It is amazing, when you don't have input from TV or social media, how you can hear things in your heart and your mind that are normally buried under the noises of everyday life. Many times, what came to the surface in the silence truly surprised me.

Whether you understand it as your own spirit of wisdom or the Spirit of a deeper voice of Love, it is good to stop and listen to what your soul wants to say to you. Mark Nepo reminds us of the need to enter into this kind of sacred, quiet reflection time. "When we are forced to stop the noise around us and in us, we begin to hear everything that is not us, and this is the beginning of humility and the renewal of our soul's energy; as only by listening to all that is larger than us can we discover and feel our place in the Universe."[29] "Through the opened heart, the world comes rushing in, the way oceans fill the smallest hole along the shore. It is the quietest sort of miracle: by simply being who we are, the world will come to fill us, to cleanse us, to baptize us, again and again."[30]

There are endless ways to nourish our spirit, and many reasons to do so. However, one of the greatest reasons for this soul searching and transformation brings us back to helping us to become better care partners. Henri had a great interest in Van Gogh and Rembrandt, reflecting often on their lives and their paintings. Here, he reminds us of how our ongoing inner search reaps benefits for others.

> There can hardly be a better image of caring than that of the artist who brings new life to people by an honest and fearless self-portrait. Rembrandt painted his sixty-three self-portraits, ... feeling that he had to enter into his own self, into his dark cellars as well as into his light rooms if he really wanted to penetrate the mystery of the human interior. ... We will never be able to really care if we are not willing to paint and repaint constantly our self-portrait ... as a service to those who are searching for some light in the midst of darkness.[31]

Questions for Reflection

1. In what ways do you currently tend to your spirit?

2. Are there new forms of self-care for your spirit that can keep you filled and inspired? What might you try to incorporate?

3. How would you describe your spiritual self?

4. Do more formal religious rituals and practices help you in your spiritual self-care? Describe them. How do they help your spirit and the way you care for others?

5. Are there any rituals or practices you would like to learn more about or take part in? If so, how could you make that happen?

Epilogue

A Lifetime of Caregiving Lessons

Writing this book has been a great gift to me. It has allowed me to focus my energy and passion in a direction that has filled my heart at a time in my life that had been marked by change and transition – and the turmoil that can go along with that. I have cherished the opportunity to share my stories and learnings with you. I hope you can also come to recognize your own stories and learnings as you reflect on your experiences of partnering in care.

In pondering a lifetime of caring, I have learned many things. I have come to understand that there is a ripple effect to caring for another, akin to tossing a stone into the water and watching the waves stream out and multiply. Each act of kindness, each word of compassion and hope flows outwards and touches not only the intended person, but so many of those connected to them. It also circles back to our own hearts and washes over us with a sense of purpose. Eventually, it sets in motion new ripples begun by carers impacted by earlier waves. It is truly an endless cycle.

I have learned that true care and compassion is both contagious and powerful: we never know how our words or our actions will affect others. Because of this, it is crucial to be nourished and cared for ourselves so we always have the capacity and ability to give others the very best of ourselves. Take good care of yourselves, as you care for others. There is only one of you, and you owe it to yourself and to those you love and serve to be healthy. This has been my personal quest, as I have strived for wellness and health in my own busy life. There are times I have been successful, and times I have failed miserably, yet the awareness of this need has kept me moving forward.

Our lives are not to be lived as solitary beings, but as interconnected tapestries woven from the wisdom, love and care of those we have been privileged to encounter along the way. Take time often to be fed and inspired by your own life experiences and care experiences. Ponder not only what you have given, but what you have received in these encounters. Let the gifts hold and carry you, especially when you feel burdened and depleted.

Henri Nouwen, Rachel Naomi Remen, Jean Vanier, Wayne Muller, Richard Rohr and many others have inspired me through their writings and their lives. They remind me, especially when I feel discouraged, that there are enriching and soulful perspectives to consider when engaging with those who are suffering, and that includes engaging with our own aching souls. Plan to be nourished and renew yourselves often. Drink in the wisdom of those who inspire you, with the riches and insights they have to share.

I am so grateful for what I have learned from my colleagues, friends and mentors over the years, and I cherish each one of them for the threads they have added to my life's tapestry. I have also grown immensely because of the people who have allowed me the privilege of caring for and accompanying them, including patients, parishioners, family and friends. Spending the last number of years working in palliative care has been an especially rich time of learning about the need to cherish every moment.

All of us will leave our own legacies, and many will remember us by how we cared for them. Something I have learned is that our universal legacy is love. Those we have loved we continue to love long after they are gone from this place. Love is our legacy in our everyday living, and love will continue to keep us connected to the hearts of those we have had the privilege to meet along the way. I believe that love is eternal – that love is what holds the universe together, and that love never dies.

I also believe that we are all born out of love and are connected in particular to the Source of Love that has created the entire universe and the human family. Many would name this source "God" or "Creator." This divine energy reminds us that all of creation is interrelated, pulling us naturally towards one another and creation itself. This belief has given me meaning and purpose in my own living along with an ability to trust and to care.

Henri Nouwen's writings in particular have helped me learn to feel comfortable in my own skin and to believe that I am unconditionally loved by this Source of Universal Love. Living my life with an energy arising out of a secure sense of being loved, rather than living out of fear and the need to please, has helped me in turn to have the freedom to be a better lover and caregiver. Although I have not always been successful, I know that I can start each day fresh and be open to whatever life has in store for me

Endnotes

Foreword

1   Henri Nouwen, *Turn My Mourning into Dancing: Finding Hope in Hard Times*, ed. Timonthy Jones (Nashville: Thomas Nelson, 2001), 12–13.

Introduction

1   Henri Nouwen, *Our Greatest Gift: A Meditation on Dying and Caring* (San Francisco: HarperSanFranciso, 1994), 51.

Chapter 1

1   Henri Nouwen, *Out of Solitude* (Notre Dame, IN: Ave Maria Press, 1974), 37–38.

2   Donald P. McNeill, Douglas A. Morrison, and Henri J. M. Nouwen, *Compassion: A Reflection on the Christian Life* (New York: Doubleday, 1983), 3.

3   Shane Sinclair et al., Sympathy, Empathy and Compassion: A Grounded Theory Study of Palliative Care Patients' Understandings, Experiences, and Preferences. *Palliative Medicine* 31:5 (2017), 444.

4   Nouwen, *Out of Solitude*, 38.

5   Mike Martin, *Meaningful Work: Rethinking Professional Ethics* (New York: Oxford University Press, 2000), 82.

6   Dr. Eric Cassel, *The Nature of Suffering and the Goals of Medicine* (New York: Oxford University Press, 2004), 31.

7   Henri Nouwen, *Here and Now: Living in the Spirit* (New York: Crossroad, 1994), 40–41.

8   Lorraine Wright, *Suffering and Spirituality: The Path to Illness Healing* (Calgary, AB: 4th Floor Press, 2017), Kindle edition, 793–807.

9   Henri Nouwen, as quoted in ibid., 813.

10 Wright, *Suffering and Spirituality*, 781.

11 McNeill, Morrison and Nouwen, *Compassion*, 38.

12 Marjorie Thompson, *Courage for Caregivers: Sustenance for the Journey* (Henri Nouwen Legacy Trust and Church Health Centre, 2017), 15.

13 Nouwen, *Here and Now*, 144.

14 Viktor Frankl, *Man's Search for Meaning* (Boston: Beacon Press, 1959), 115.

15 Brent D. Rosso, Kathryn H. Dekas and Amy Wrzesniewski, *On the Meaning of Work: A Theoretical Integration and Review* (Berkeley, CA: Elsevier, 2010).

16 Ibid.

17 Wishful Thinking: A Seeker's ABC, 119, http://www.calledthejourney.com/blog/2014/12/17/frederick-buechner-on-calling.

18 A. Wrzeniewski, C. R. McCauley, P. Rozin and B. Schwartz, Jobs, Careers, and Callings: People's Relations to Their Work. *Journal of Research in Personality* 31 (1997), 21–33.

19 Thich Nhat Hanh, *The Heart of the Buddha's Teaching* (New York: Broadway Books, 1998), 102.

20 Henri Nouwen, *Bread for the Journey: A Daybook of Wisdom and Faith* (San Francisco: HarperSanFrancisco, 1997), January 17.

21 Nouwen, *Bread for the Journey*, March 10.

22 Henri Nouwen, *Discernment: Reading the Signs of Daily Life*, with Michael J. Christensen and Rebecca J. Laird (Henri Nouwen Legacy Trust and Harper Collins, 2013), viii.

23 Henri Nouwen, *Making All Things New: An Invitation to the Spiritual Life* (New York: Harper and Row, 1901), 33.

24 Nouwen, *Bread for the Journey*, August 9.

25 Henri Nouwen, *The Inner Voice of Love: A Journey through Anguish to Freedom* (New York: Doubleday, 1996), 6.

Chapter 2

1   Saki Santorelli, *Heal Thy Self: Lessons on Mindfulness in Medicine* (Washington, DC: Bell Tower, 1999), 20.

2   Henri Nouwen, *Here and Now: Living in the Spirit* (New York: Crossroad, 1994), 107.

3   https://www.who.int/about/who-we-are/frequently-asked-questions

4   Rachel Naomi Remen, *Kitchen Table Wisdom* (New York: Penguin, 2006), 217.

5   Henri Nouwen, *Bread for the Journey: A Daybook of Wisdom and Faith* (San Francisco: HarperSanFrancisco, 1997), July 8.

6   Pema Chodron, *The Places that Scare You: A Guide to Fearlessness in Difficult Times*, pg n/a.

7   Henri Nouwen, *Care and the Elderly* – a pamphlet adapted from a speech delivered June 6, 1975 (The Henri Nouwen Legacy Trust, 2008), 8–10.

8   Nouwen, *Bread for the Journey*, July 10.

9 Michelle O'Rourke and Eugene Dufour, *Embracing the End of Life: Help for Those Who Accompany the Dying* (Toronto: Novalis, 2012), 39.

10 Jane Powell, *Grieving in the Context of a Community of Differently-Abled People: The Experience of L'Arche Daybreak*, in Cox, Bendiksen and Stevenson, eds., *Complicated Grieving and Bereavement* (Baywood, 2002), 9.

11 Walter Gaffney and Henri J. M. Nouwen, *Aging* (New York: Doubleday, 1974), 153.

12 Remen, *Kitchen Table Wisdom*, 143–44.

13 Nouwen, *Bread for the Journey*, March 11.

14 Shane Sinclair, Mia-Bernadine Torres, Shelley Raffin-Bouchal, et al., Compassion Training in Healthcare: What Are Patients' Perspectives on Training Healthcare Providers? *BMC Medical Education* 16 (2016), https://bmcmededuc.biomedcentral.com/articles/10.1186/s12909-016-0695-0.

15 Shane Sinclair, Thomas F. Hack, Shelley Raffin-Bouchal, et al., What Are Healthcare Providers' Understandings and Experiences of Compassion? The Healthcare Compassion Model: A Grounded Theory Study of Healthcare Providers in Canada, *BMJ Open* 8:3 (2018), https://bmjopen.bmj.com/content/8/3/e019701.

16 Henri Nouwen, *Reaching Out: The Three Movements of the Spiritual Life* (New York: Doubleday, 1975), 95.

17 Ibid., 92–93.

Chapter 3

1 Henri Nouwen, *A Spirituality of Caregiving*, J. Mogabgab ed. (Henri Nouwen Legacy Trust and Upper Room Books, 2011), 26.

2 Henri Nouwen, *Befriending Death*, an address to the National Catholic AIDS Network, Chicago, July 1995 (Henri Nouwen Legacy Trust), 7.

3 Henri Nouwen, *With Burning Hearts* (New York: Orbis, 1994), 29.

4 Henri Nouwen, *Bread for the Journey: A Daybook of Wisdom and Faith* (San Francisco: HarperSanFrancisco, 1997), January 5.

5 Henri Nouwen, *Our Greatest Gift: A Meditation on Dying and Caring* (San Francisco: Harper San Francisco, 1994), 57.

6 Henri Nouwen, *Sabbatical Journey: The Diary of His Final Year* (New York: Crossroad, 1998), 143.

7 Etty Hillesum, *An Interrupted Life: The Diaries of Etty Hillesum 1941–1943* (New York: Pantheon, 1983), 185.

8 Nouwen, *Bread for the Journey*, January 6.

9 Nouwen, *A Spirituality of Caregiving*, 17.

10 Ibid.

11 Ibid., 38–39.

12 Nouwen, *Our Greatest Gift,* 14.

13 Ibid., 60.

14 H.M. Chochinov, T. Hack, T. Hassard, et al., Dignity in the Terminally Ill: A Cross-sectional, Cohort Study, *Lancet* 360:9350 (2002), 2026–30.

15 Harvey Chochinov, *Dignity Therapy: Final Words for Final Days* (New York: Oxford University Press, 2012), 41.

16 Ibid., 30.

17 H.M. Chochinov, Dignity and the Essence of Medicine: The A, B, C, & D of Dignity Conserving Care, *BMJ* 335:7612 (2007), 184–87, https://www.ncbi.nlm.nih.gov/pmc/articles/PMC1934489.

18 Nouwen, *Our Greatest Gift,* 63.

19 C.R. Figley, ed., *Compassion Fatigue: Coping with Secondary Traumatic Stress Disorder in Those Who Treat the Traumatized* (New York: Bunner/Mazel, 1995), 1.

20 Rachel Naomi Remen, *Kitchen Table Wisdom* (New York: Penguin, 2006), 1.

21 Françoise Mathieu, *The Compassion Fatigue Workbook* (New York: Routledge, 2012), 8, 9.

22 Interview with Henri Nouwen, *University of Notre Dame Alumni Continuing Education,* 1996, video recording: viewed at the Henri J. M. Nouwen Archives and Research Collection, John M. Kelly Library, University of St. Michael's College, Toronto.

23 Wendy Austin, E. Sharon Brintnell, Erika Goble, et al., *Lying Down in the Ever-Falling Snow: Canadian Health Professionals' Experience of Compassion Fatigue* (Waterloo, ON: Wilfrid Laurier University Press, 2013), 43.

Chapter 4

1 Marjorie Thompson, *Courage for Caregivers, Sustenance for the Journey* (Henri Nouwen Legacy Trust and Church Health Centre, 2017), 65.

2 Donald P. McNeill, Douglas A. Morrison, and Henri J. M. Nouwen, *Compassion: A Reflection on the Christian Life* (New York: Doubleday, 1983), 90–91.

3 Ibid., 95.

4 Ibid., 98–100.

5 Ibid., 96.

6 Henri Nouwen, *The Return of the Prodigal Son* (New York: Doubleday, 1992), 85.

7 Henri Nouwen, *Can You Drink the Cup* (Notre Dame, IN: Ave Maria Press, 1996), 56.

8 Henri Nouwen, *Bread for the Journey: A Daybook of Wisdom and Faith* (San Francisco: HarperSanFrancisco, 1997), February 1.

9 Henri Nouwen, *Here and Now: Living in the Spirit* (New York: Crossroad, 1994), 102–103.

10 Madeleine L'Engle, *Walking on Water: Reflections on Faith and Art* (New York: Convergent Books, 2016), 182.

11 Jean Vanier, *Becoming Human* (Toronto: House of Anansi Press, 2008).

12 Henri Nouwen, *Adam: God's Beloved* (Maryknoll, NY: Orbis, 1997), 101.

13 Henri Nouwen, *Our Greatest Gift: A Meditation on Dying and Caring* (San Francisco: Harper San Francisco, 1994), xv–xvi.

14 Henri Nouwen, "Henri Nouwen on Death and Aging," *Cross Point* (Fall 1995), 4.

15 Nouwen, *Our Greatest Gift*, 4.

16 Frank Ostaseski, *The Five Invitations: Discovering What Death Can Teach Us About Living Fully* (New York: Flatiron Books, 2017), 121.

17 Ibid., 121, 122.

18 Rachel Naomi Remen, "Helping, Fixing, or Serving?" *Lion's Roar: Buddhist Wisdom for Our Time* (August 6, 2017), https://www.lionsroar.com/helping-fixing-or-serving.

19 Ostaseski, *The Five Invitations*, 128.

20 Rachel Naomi Remen, "A Revolution in Healthcare," *Lion's Roar: Buddhist Wisdom for Our Time* (July, 1, 1999), https://www.lionsroar.com/a-revolution-in-healthcare.

21 Matt Licata and Jeff Foster, "Love is the Only True Medicine," Wandering Yogi Press, forthcoming. Used with permission.

22 Nouwen, *Bread for the Journey*, June 26.

23 Ibid., August 25.

Chapter 5

1 Brené Brown, *The Gifts of Imperfection: Let Go of Who You Think You're Supposed to Be and Embrace Who You Are* (Center City, MN: Hazelden, 2010), 20.

2 Henri Nouwen, *Our Greatest Gift: A Meditation on Dying and Caring* (San Francisco: Harper San Francisco, 1994), 58–63.

3 Henri Nouwen, *Life of the Beloved: Spiritual Living in a Secular World* (New York: Crossroad, 1992), 72–73.

4 Henri Nouwen, *Making All Things New: An Invitation to the Spiritual Life* (New York: Harper and Row, 1981), 88.

5 Henri Nouwen, *Bread for the Journey: A Daybook of Wisdom and Faith* (San Francisco: HarperSanFrancisco, 1997), March 13.

6 Nouwen, *Our Greatest Gift*, 84–85.

7 Kristin Neff and Christopher Germer, *The Mindful Self-Compassion Workbook* (New York: Guilford Press, 2018), 9.

8 Ibid., 22.

9 Ibid., 31.

10 Ibid., 138.

11 Ibid., 140.

12 Milton Mayeroff, *On Caring* (New York: Harper and Row, 1971), 51, 52.

13 Wayne Muller, *A Life of Being, Having and Doing Enough* (New York: Crown, 2010), 3, 5.

14 Ibid., 119.

15 Henri Nouwen, *Turn My Mourning into Dancing: Finding Hope in Hard Times*, Timothy Jones, ed. (New York: Thomas Nelson, 2001), 12–13.

16 Mark Nepo, *Seven Thousand Ways to Listen: Staying Close to What Is Sacred* (New York: Simon and Schuster, 2012), 287.

17 Michelle O'Rourke and Eugene Dufour, *Embracing the End of Life* (Toronto: Novalis, 2012), 20, 21.

18 Henri Nouwen, *A Spirituality of Caregiving*, J. Mogabgab ed. (Henri Nouwen Legacy Trust and Upper Room Books, 2011), 52.

19 Mark Nepo, *The Book of Awakening: Having the Life You Want by Being Present to the Life You Have* (Newburyport, MA: Conari Press, 2000), 388.

20 Jon Kabat-Zinn, *Mindfulness for Beginners* (Boulder, CO: Sounds True, 2016), 1, 2.

21 Neff and Germer, *The Mindful Self-Compassion Workbook*, 45, 46.

22 Frank Ostaseski, *The Five Invitations: Discovering What Death Can Teach Us About Living Fully* (New York: Flatiron Books, 2017), 212.

23 Mark Nepo, https://www.azquotes.com/author/18173-Mark_Nepo.

24 Henri Nouwen, *Out of Solitude* (Notre Dame, IN: Ave Maria Press, 1974), 26.

25 Wayne Muller, *Sabbath: Restoring the Sacred Rhythm of Rest* (New York: Bantam Books, 1999), 1, 3.

26 Parker Palmer, *On the Brink of Everything: Grace, Gravity and Getting Old* (San Francisco: Berrett-Koehler Publishers, 2018), 138.

27 Ibid., 137, 138.

28 Henri Nouwen, *A Cry for Mercy: Prayers from the Genesee* (New York: Doubleday, 1981), 149.

29 Mark Nepo, https://www.azquotes.com/author/18173-Mark_Nepo?p=2.

30 Mark Nepo, *The Book of Awakening: Having the Life You Want by Being Present to the Life You Have,* Gift Edition (Newburyport, MA: Conari Press, 2011), 111.

31 Walter Gaffney and Henri J. M. Nouwen, *Aging* (New York: Doubleday, 1974), 95.

Helpful Resources

Besides the many books and articles that are listed in the endnotes, some other tremendous resources are available to support your care practice. These are some of my personal favourites, including websites and articles that I did not cite.

Websites

Henri Nouwen Society – www.henrinouwen.org – caregiver resources; books; events

Compassion Fatigue – www.compassionfatigue.org – access to resources and tools, including the Professional Quality of Life (ProQoL) self-test

Tend Academy – www.tendacademy.ca (formerly www.compassionfatigue.ca) – has resources for compassion fatigue developed by Canadian Françoise Mathieu and Dr. Patricia Fisher

Self-Care Inventory – https://www.nami.org/getattachment/Extranet/Education,-Training-and-Outreach-Programs/Signature-Classes/NAMI-Homefront/HF-Additional-Resources/HF15AR6SelfCare.pdf

National Alliance on Mental Illness: www.nami.org (Look for the NAMI Homefront Additional Resources page; the inventory is part of Class 6 at the bottom of the page.)

Mindfulness – www.mindful.org – articles and resources on developing mindfulness

Self-Compassion – www.selfcompassion.org – Dr. Kristen Neff's website

Canadian Virtual Hospice – www.virtualhospice.ca – professional resources/articles on a number of topics

Articles

Halifax, J. (2014). G.R.A.C.E. for Nurses: Cultivating Compassion in Nurse/patient Interactions. *Journal of Nursing Education and Practice, 4*(1).

Sanso, N. et al. (2015). Palliative Care Professionals' Inner Life: Exploring the Relationships Among Awareness, Self-Care, and Compassion Satisfaction and Fatigue, Burnout, and Coping with Death. *Journal Pain and Symptom Management, 50* (2), 200–207.

Sinclair, S et al. (2017). Compassion Fatigue: A Meta-narrative Review of the Healthcare Literature. *Palliative Medicine, 31*(5), 437–47.

Wagaman, M. A. et al. (2015). The Role of Empathy in Burnout, Compassion Satisfaction, and Secondary Traumatic Stress among Social Workers. *Social Work, 60* (30), 201–209.

Zeidner, M. and D. Hadar (2014). Some Individual Difference Predictors of Professional Well-being and Satisfaction of Health Professionals. *Personality and Individual Differences, 65*, 91–95.

Books

Caregiver Stress and Staff Support in Illness, Dying and Bereavement. Edited by Irene Renzenbrink. New York: Oxford University Press, 2011.

Whole Person Care: A New Paradigm for the 21st Century. Edited by Tom A. Hutchinson. New York: Springer, 2011.

Permissions